DATE DUE

NO 5'99			

Demco, Inc. 38-293

284

Western Wild Flowers
and Their Stories

Books By

Charles Francis Saunders

Western Wild Flowers
and Their Stories
Under the Sky in California
With the Flowers and Trees in California
Trees and Shrubs of California Gardens
The Western Flower Guide
Southern Sierras of California
Useful Wild Plants of the United States and Canada
Finding the Worth While in California
Story of Carmelita

Western Wild Flowers and Their Stories

By

CHARLES FRANCIS SAUNDERS

Doubleday, Doran & Company, Inc.

GARDEN CITY, NEW YORK

1933

Press, GARDEN CITY, N. Y., U. S. A.

Gilias in Sequoia National Park

Contents

v

CONTENTS

Illustrations

Introduction

IN VIEW of the number of existing books on the wild flowers of the Pacific slope, it may be well to explain why the public should be invited to invest in another.

One winter's evening many years ago in Philadelphia I heard the late Dr. Joseph T. Rothrock lecture on wild plants to a group of people who, like myself at that time, knew nothing of botany but did love flowers. One remark above others awakened my interest. "The object of learning a plant's name," said he, "is to have a key to its literature." That every wild flower—even the humblest weed—has a literature was news to me then, and, as I have since found, is news to most people still. This literature, in many cases, may be no more than a bare description published when the name is given (and if there is anything barer or bleaker to the average man than a description couched in the terms of science, I do not know it); or it may be a treatise, formal or discursive, on the plant's rôle in the human drama; for plants have been the comrades of man from the dawn of time, taking part in his struggle for life, in his work and in his play; given a place in his myths, religions and histories; in his arts, medicine and economics.

The plan of the present volume has been to assemble facts respecting characteristic wild flowers of the Pacific States, and especially California, that are likely to be of interest to the general plant lover and particularly to that class which loves them for their esthetic graces and human associations rather than for their anatomical make-up and workings. Our Pacific coast is still so young that its plant literature is relatively meager; nevertheless, the records and journals of the early and later travelers, the incidental notes of scientific workers and the delightful memories of the older generation of Spanish Californians furnish a considerable fund of human interest in connection with our flora, and from such sources, largely, the following chapters have been drawn.

I hope the non-botanical reader will forgive me for all the Latin and Greek plant names injected into the narrative, but in the interest of certitude there seemed no way of escaping them. No attempt has been made to provide means of identification of species. For that, Jepson's *Manual of Flowering Plants of California* and Piper and Beattie's *Flora of the Northwest Coast* may be consulted. The scholarly *Illustrated Flora of the Pacific States*, by Dr. LeRoy Abrams, in course of publication, will also be most useful.

I would here express my appreciation of help generously accorded by many friends and correspondents, among them Miss Alice Eastwood of the California Academy of Sciences, Mrs. Georgiana Parks Ballard, Paso Robles, California, Doña Matilde Carteri and Mr. Edward Barber, Santa Barbara, Dr. Willis Linn Jepson of the University of California, Dr. LeRoy Abrams of Stanford University, Dr. Philip S. Munz of Pomona College, and Sir Arthur W. Hill of the Royal Botanic Gardens, Kew. To my kinsman Mr. Edward H. Parry, Wyncote, Pennsylvania, I am especially indebted for patient research among sources not accessible to me in person, and to my wife for numerous sympathetic suggestions.

Western Wild Flowers
and Their Stories

with a rancho whose three square leagues, *poco más ó menos*, as the old deeds ran, spread fair about the Sierra Madre's skirts. Out of it and its poppy fields fifty-odd years ago the land upon which the city of Pasadena now stands was taken; and many another tract as well; so that now our California poppy would be little more than a tale that was told over much of that old rancho's area, were it not for the gardens that harbor the flower's domesticated descendants.

The first botanist to note the existence of the California poppy was Archibald Menzies, surgeon and naturalist of Captain George Vancouver's famous world-girdling expedition, which touched at various points on our Pacific coast in the years 1792 and 1793. This industrious collector discovered the plant at several stations in California and believed it to be a variety of the Old World celandine. He gave seeds of it to the Royal Botanic Gardens at Kew, where they were sown. The result was a number of weakling plants which perished untimely without issue. Dried specimens were distributed among the herbariums of various European naturalists, in the dusty seclusion of which the beautiful flower, in spite of its obviously being a novelty, lay unchristened until another botanist, following in the footsteps of Menzies twenty-odd years later, collected it anew and gave to the world a description of it and a name. This was Adelbert von Chamisso, poet-naturalist of the Russian scientific expedition under the command of Otto von Kotzebue, which lay a few days in the harbor of San Francisco in November, 1816. Botanizing in California in November is rather disappointing business; nevertheless, the bleak sands of the peninsula yielded a harvest of seeds, among which were those of

Western Wild Flowers
and Their Stories

TO
EDWARD BARBER
Friend of Half a Lifetime
Whose Enthusiastic Coöperation
in the Preparation of This Volume
Is Gratefully Acknowledged
the Author Affectionately
Inscribes It

CHAPTER I

*Of the Golden State's Floral Emblem; How the
World Learned about It; and Somewhat of Other
Pacific Coast Poppies.*

O<small>NCE</small> upon a time—and it is not so long ago, either,
for there are eyewitnesses to the fact living today—the
attention of the traveler by sea along the southern
California coast in late winter or early spring would
be attracted by a remarkable spectacle. For mile upon
mile the dimpled foothills of the Coast Range and its
seaward stretching mesas would glow as if on fire from
the limitless fields of copper-hued poppies, open
mouthed to the sun. Tradition has it that in Spanish
days sailors on the ships off the coast had their imagina-
tions so stirred by the phenomenon that they nicknamed this country, as they had long before dubbed
another bit of America—*La Tierra del Fuego*, the Land
of Fire. Others, they say, called this flowery carpet *La
Sabanilla de San Pasqual*, that is, the Altar-cloth of
St. Pascal, that pious shepherd lad of Old Spain, who,
tending his flocks in the open fields remote from church
or priest, would kneel among the wild flowers and be
rapt of the Spirit into heavenly communion.

How much of fiction and what of truth these old tales
embody it is not for me to say; but the fact is beyond
dispute that when California was incorporated into the
United States, San Pasqual's name was found identified

with a rancho whose three square leagues, *poco más ó menos,* as the old deeds ran, spread fair about the Sierra Madre's skirts. Out of it and its poppy fields fifty-odd years ago the land upon which the city of Pasadena now stands was taken; and many another tract as well; so that now our California poppy would be little more than a tale that was told over much of that old rancho's area, were it not for the gardens that harbor the flower's domesticated descendants.

The first botanist to note the existence of the California poppy was Archibald Menzies, surgeon and naturalist of Captain George Vancouver's famous world-girdling expedition, which touched at various points on our Pacific coast in the years 1792 and 1793. This industrious collector discovered the plant at several stations in California and believed it to be a variety of the Old World celandine. He gave seeds of it to the Royal Botanic Gardens at Kew, where they were sown. The result was a number of weakling plants which perished untimely without issue. Dried specimens were distributed among the herbariums of various European naturalists, in the dusty seclusion of which the beautiful flower, in spite of its obviously being a novelty, lay unchristened until another botanist, following in the footsteps of Menzies twenty-odd years later, collected it anew and gave to the world a description of it and a name. This was Adelbert von Chamisso, poet-naturalist of the Russian scientific expedition under the command of Otto von Kotzebue, which lay a few days in the harbor of San Francisco in November, 1816. Botanizing in California in November is rather disappointing business; nevertheless, the bleak sands of the peninsula yielded a harvest of seeds, among which were those of our poppy. Four years later, in a collection of scientific papers, a description of the plant was published, and the world was forever more to know Menzies's foundling as Chamisso's *Eschscholtzia californica*, a name given in honor of Dr. Johann Friedrich Eschscholz, surgeon of Kotzebue's party and a lifelong friend of Chamisso.

More than this, however, was necessary to effect the flower's popularity with the rank and file of plant lovers. This thing needful came about when David Douglas arrived on the Pacific coast in the interests of the London Horticultural Society, whose members were desirous of enriching their gardens by drawing upon the delightful wild gardens of California and the northwest coast, the fame of whose floral and sylvan wealth had begun to impress Europe. Douglas was both a botanist and a practical gardener, and among the new plants that daily came to his hand there was, one day, this golden poppy, which he found abundant on the sandy plains bordering the Willamette River, known in that day as the Multnomah. The seeds that he sent to England in 1825 proved productive, and the plant, taking kindly to English conditions, quickly made a place for itself in the affections of the gardening public, a place that it holds to this day. In Australia and India the flower has leapt the garden fence and become naturalized. Cultivated varieties, including a double form, are now numerous and are offered by seedsmen. This is not to be wondered at when it is realized that in nature *Eschscholtzia californica* is one of the most variable of species, both in character of foliage and color of flower. The latter varies from light yellow to deep orange or copper.

Besides *E. californica*, which is a perennial and

abundant throughout the length of the state west of the
Sierra Nevada below 2,000 feet elevation, and is honored
as the state's floral emblem, there are half a dozen
species that are annual and of more or less restricted
distribution. Their differences from the well known
perennial species are less important to the layman than
to the botanist and need not be specified here except
in the case of one. This is *Eschscholtzia minutiflora*,
which is native to the deserts of California, Nevada
and Arizona and their borders—a dainty little affair,
a few inches high, with numerous minute flowers a
quarter inch across or even less.

All the Eschscholtzias have a watery juice, which
possesses something of the narcotic quality that dis-
tinguishes its famous oriental cousin the opium poppy.
The Indians somehow discovered this drowsy property,
and in old times made use of the fresh root to stop the
ache of a hollow tooth, while an extract from it had
some vogue as a liniment to relieve headache.[1] The
foliage was also cooked sometimes as a vegetable, and
Philip Sparkman, a reliable recorder of aboriginal ways
who once kept a store near Valley Green, San Diego
County, California, has testified to a curious use of
the flowers by the Luiseños—they were chewed with
chewing gum! Among the Spanish Californians the
California poppy was called by a variety of names, as
amapola, torosa, copa de oro (gold cup), *dormidera*
(sleepy one, for the flowers close at night), and had a
reputation for making the hair grow. The petals were
mixed with olive oil or suet, cooked over a slow fire
and strained. The result was called *pomada de amapola*
and rubbed, in fullness of faith, on thinning hair.

[1]Chesnut: *Plants Used by the Indians of Mendocino County.*

After so much, it is very disturbing to learn that except in a broad sense Eschscholtzia is not a poppy at all. It is merely one member in a considerable family to which the true poppy gives title. In strictness, the name poppy belongs only to plants of the genus *Papaver*, a venerable word that has come down to us unchanged from antiquity, Virgil's *soporiferum papaver*, the sleep bearer. To the purist the real California poppy is quite another plant, *Papaver californicum*, which a great many Californians live and die without ever seeing, for it is to be listed, like so many things in California, among the unusual. Indeed, it was not until 1886 that it was brought to the attention of the botanical world. In the spring of that year one John Spence, a keen-eyed Englishman who conducted a florist shop and nursery in Santa Barbara, was taking a jaunt in the Santa Ynez Mountains, and traversing a place that had been desolated by fire the year before, he picked up, in passing, some flowers of a plant unknown to him and sent them to Dr. Asa Gray at Harvard for identification, he at that time being the great American authority on matters botanical. From this scanty material, Dr. Gray was inclined to believe the plant the common corn poppy of Europe, which might be expected to occur in old wheat fields, although no one had ever reported seeing it in such places in California. The receipt of better specimens later on, gathered far away from any trail, made it clear that here was a new and interesting indigenous species, and it was given the name under which it is now known. Its occurrence is mainly in the lower end of the state, and it is to be looked for most hopefully in mid-spring on chaparral lands that have been cleared or burned over the previous year. It may be recognized by its showy red or orange-scarlet flower, solitary upon a tall stem (each glowing petal touched at the base with green), succeeded by the trimmest of seed pods—a charming bit of plant architecture, vase-like with fluted sides, capped with the spreading summit of the pistil, and filled with black seeds of unbelievable smallness, mere grains of dust. Of similar appearance is its cousin the wind poppy (*Papaver heterophyllum*, the vari-form leaved), which is found on grassy hillsides and valley lands from central California southward. Its petals, though of much the same color as those of *P. californicum*, are dark spotted at the base, and exceedingly fleeting, so that a touch may be enough to startle them into falling. They are best enjoyed undisturbed.

Also of the Poppy cousinhood, as you might guess from the modest, drooping buds, is that charming spring flower whose common name cream-cups describes it quite perfectly, if you have country cream in mind. It was one of Archibald Menzies's discoveries, and dried specimens presented by him to his botanical friends remained lost to sight in their herbariums and undescribed, as was the fate of so many of that pioneer collector's finds; but in the 1830's Douglas discovered the plant again, and it received recognition under the name by which it now goes, *Platystemon californicus*. The seeds of it which Douglas sent from California to his employers, the London Horticultural Society, were without instructions as to requirements, and probably from improper planting failed to establish the plant horticulturally, and so it was for a time lost to foreign gardens. Later introductions were more successful, and today it thrives in happy expatriation in many a European garden, as well as California. An interesting feature of this pretty flower is one few who gather it ever notice—that is, the remarkable arrangement of the mature seed vessel, which takes the aspect of a tiny, bewhiskered ear of green corn from which the husk has been stripped. To the lover of Flora's quieter moods, few sights in nature or in a garden are fuller of charm than a company of these chaste little cups of bloom open to the sun and in their midst the blushing buds awaiting their turn on the morrow.

A princess of the Poppy family in California is the famous Matilija, the stems at times as much as eight feet tall, and the glorious, golden-centered flowers with crêpy white petals measuring four or five inches across. It owes its common name (which you are to pronounce as though written *matil'ihah*) to its occurrence in Matilija Cañon in Ventura County. While not to be counted a common wilding, it may be expected in May or June in several parts of coastal southern California and on down into Lower California as far as San Quentin. It particularly enjoys the sandy washes of cañon bottoms, but accommodates itself also to the harsher conditions of dry hillsides. It was first brought to notice by Dr. Thomas Coulter, an Englishman who visited California in 1831 and spent two years in the province, industriously botanizing from San Francisco to San Diego. In the spring of 1832 he made a notable trip from San Gabriel to the Colorado River by way of San Felipe Pass, and so became the botanical discoverer of the Colorado Desert, whose remarkable flora was at that season at its best. It appears to have been on this journey that he encountered this regal flower. The specimens that he carried home from California—there are said to have been about 50,000 of them, representing over 1,500 species—gathered dust for many years, and it was not until after Coulter's death that a description of this famous beauty was published and a name given. Coulter, it seems, had a friend, **T. Romney Robinson,** the Irish "astronomer of Armagh," and the botanist who wrote the description, W. H. Harvey, also an Irishman, made a clever double play by naming the plant for them both at one stroke—*Romneya Coulteri.*

As is the case with so many California wildings, Romneya has been introduced into gardens both of this country and Europe. I am told that in Santa Barbara it was already a garden plant in Spanish times, and was modestly known as mission poppy. In the view of the Americans, when they arrived, this was considered quite inadequate, and with characteristic grandiloquence they substituted "giant California white poppy." William Robinson, in his *English Flower Garden,* declares it to be "the fairest plant that ever came to our land from that country of flowers, California." On the occasion of the flower's first public exhibition in London, in 1888, it made a sensation. "So enraptured was I," wrote an English correspondent of an American horticultural journal at the time, "that I sat by the plant an hour. . . . Who could begrudge time and labor to bring such a fine flower to perfection!" Even a beautiful flower, however, can become a weed, if it grows where not wanted, and the Matilija poppy has been known to invade orchards in the fruitful Santa Clara Valley, and because of its aggressive way of increasing by suckering has become a nuisance in places. If you are young and patient you may enjoy raising it from seed. People who have tried say that at least two

years pass before germination. In England it is sometimes called tree poppy, I hear, but this term is used
in California to designate another member of the Poppy
tribe, *Dendromecon rigida*, a rather abundant shrub of
dry hills in various parts of the state, with willowy
leaves and flowers of a golden yellow. This was one of
Douglas's discoveries, who hoped to see it adorning
English gardens, but its wild blood is not easily tamed,
and it is disposed to pine under the confinement of
garden walls.

Every spring stories get abroad about Matilija poppies that someone has seen in bloom upon the desert,
which would indeed be news if true; but always investigation develops the fact that what was really seen was
not the Matilija poppy (which has no taste at all for
deserts) but its cousin the prickly poppy, *Argemone
platyceras* or *intermedia corymbosa*, the *chicalote* of the
Mexicans. One cannot blame the uncritical for confusing
the two flowers, particularly when botanizing at thirty
or forty miles an hour from an automobile, as the
amiable art is nowadays so often practised, for the
blossoms are surprisingly alike. The plants themselves,
however, are unmistakably dissimilar, the stems of the
Matilija poppy being smooth, while Argemone's bristle
with prickly yellow spines, which make the common
name most apt.

In sandy washes of the Mohave Desert in April or
May blooms the tiniest of the Poppy family, an inch
high, its petite white flowers lifted on thread-like stems,
of which there are many rising from a dense tuft of
fat little leaves a quarter inch long. It bears the pleasantly alliterative name *Canbya candida*—a demure
pigmy of a creature that holds its course through wind

and sandy weather, cheek by jowl with giant yuccas and shaggy cacti, blooming its tiny blooms and setting its minute seeds as importantly as though the whole world depended on the outcome. It is one of those modest plantlings which if you ever see at all will be by the accident of a wandering eye, as you sit nibbling a sandwich, perhaps, or stretch yourself along the ground for a siesta. The story of its discovery is this: In the spring of 1876 a trio of botanists, Dr. C. C. Parry, Dr. Edward Palmer, and Mr. J. G. Lemmon, spent several months together in the San Bernardino Mountains and vicinity, then almost a virgin field for plant collectors, and on a day in May, while the party was exploring the borders of the Mohave River where it breaks from the mountains into the desert, Dr. Palmer caught sight of this Lilliputian with its bright white flowers and knew it for something undescribed. The flowers are remarkable for lasting many days, opening each morning at sunrise and, the day's duties done, closing each evening at sunset. On the last evening the petals fold themselves to permanent rest over the globular little seed vessel, which the discoverer likened to a pearl. By unanimous consent Dr. Parry dedicated the genus to the party's "common friend and worthy fellow botanist, William M. Canby, Esq., of Wilmington, Delaware"—a genial banker, 3,000 miles away, with a soul for flowers, particularly Eriogonums, that is, wild buckwheats, to the world's knowledge of which he contributed greatly.

CHAPTER II

Of Roses of Castile, Toyon Pudding and Other Matters; with Some Particulars about Frederick Pursh.

W<small>E ARRIVED</small> this day," writes Fray Juan Crespi in his journal of the first white men's expedition on California soil—the date is a day of July, 1769, and the place is a few leagues north of San Diego—"we arrived this day in a very beautiful *cañada* or valley, on seeing which it appeared not otherwise than a cultivated or sown field, because of its much verdure. . . . We descended into this valley and saw that its verdure was of wild gourds, very leafy, and many wild rose bushes." You see Fray Juan had an eye for flowers, and as we turn the pages of the quaint old diary we find further mention of wild roses, which greeted the wayfarers on arroyo banks and beside "eyes of water," as they called the springs. *Rosas de Castilla*, roses of Castile, the diarist denominated them, so like were they to the wild roses of the far-away homeland. Thirty years later, you find Padre Peyri of Mission San Luis Rey telling of them as "wild roses of Castile," and even at this day in remote parts of California you may hear the same term given by Spanish-speaking people to this same wilding.

The first botanist to collect the California wild rose seems to have been Adelbert von Chamisso with Kotzebue's Russian expedition at the port of San Fran-

11

cisco in 1816, and it was given "the baptism of science" as *Rosa californica*. It is the commonest of half a dozen species occurring wild in the state, and is found, sometimes extensive thickets of it, from San Diego County to the Siskiyous. One day Crespi was ravished by the sight of a spray upon which he counted six open blossoms and twelve buds, and notes the whole eighteen in his diary as an event of real importance. Others, however, have found better since, as many as forty in a single cluster. Prodigality of bloom is, in fact, a characteristic of *R. californica;* the other species native to the state as, for instance, the dainty little redwood rose that gems the twilight trail-sides of the coast forests northward from Monterey, or the Mohave rose native to certain desert borders; these bear their flowers solitarily, or at most two or three together. *Rosa del campo* is the customary name by which the Spanish Californians call their wild rose, and the bright red hips or fruits are *macuatas.* These it was one of the joys of childhood in a simpler age to pluck and eat. Spanish housewives would sometimes cook them slightly in "just enough water, no more" (with such exactness did my motherly informant word the recipe!). Then they would be sprinkled with sugar, or not, as one preferred, a little of the liquor in which they were cooked poured over them, and one fell to. So wholesome a little fruit, in spite of its stoniness and dryness in the natural state, could hardly have failed to enter into the dietary of Indians and pioneers. At any rate, I find Padre Font, diarist of the famous Anza expedition from Mexico to the founding of San Francisco, gathering them from winter bushes and eating them out of hand, with relish.

The Rose family is a very large one, of wide distribution in the world, and, as in all large families, not all branches are "in society"; so you may be sure Queen Rose has her share of poor relations—plant folk of more or less humble station from an ornamental standpoint, though filling useful, respectable rôles in the business of life, some even making modest history of a sort, worthy of record. There is, to begin with, the chamise or greasewood, *Adenostoma fasciculatum.* The most abundant shrub of the foothills and lower mountain slopes, it is found sometimes mixing with other shrubs but often in exclusive stands of its own, square miles in extent, encasing the hillsides and ridges with a close-knit jacket of olive green, which is lightened in late spring by snowy spires of bloom, resolvable under close inspection into myriads of tiny white single roses. The general look of the plant, with its short needle-like leaves in little bunches along the stems, suggests heather. Its miniature forests are of inestimable value in conserving the winter rainfall in situations too harsh for trees. The vitality and pluck of the sturdy shrub under adverse conditions are amazing. As though it were not enough to be set down for life to draw sustenance from the midst of unresponsive rocks and gravel, and denied the refreshment of rain for six or eight consecutive months out of twelve, the curse of recurring fires has been visited upon the pigmy groves from time immemorial. The evidence is that long before the white man came with his fire-belching engines, his matches and cigarettes, fires have periodically swept the chaparral cover of the hills—fires originating from natural causes, as by lightning, or started by Indians' carelessness around their camps, or by Indian design for the purpose of driving game from its covert. Yet those fires were, as are fires today, only superficial in their effect upon the chamise, leaving the root unhurt. Surprisingly soon the butt of the charred stem becomes the parent of a brood of lusty green shoots, which in five or six years will pretty thoroughly have replaced the killed stem and branches. The effect of repeated fires on the root crown is curious. This becomes bulbously enlarged at the level of the ground, and if dug up with a foot or two of the vertical tap root attached looks like some aboriginal war club.

In clearing chaparral areas for building sites or agricultural operations, quantities of chamise roots used to be grubbed up and used as fuel. They burn with great heat and make lasting coals, though I believe the name greasewood has nothing to do with this, but arises from the fierce way the resinous foliage burns when summer or autumnal fires race and roar through the dry scrub. Chamise, that other vernacular word for the shrub, is an abbreviation of *chamiso* applied to it by Spanish-speaking people, who seem to have got it from the Indians.[1] Some tribes were in the habit of making the foreshafts of their arrows from the hard *chamiso* stems, the main shaft being of some lighter growth such as reed or wild rye. The plant was first brought to the attention of the world by the botanists of Captain Beechey's expedition, which touched upon the California coast in 1827 and carried specimens to England from "sandy plains in the Bay of Monterrey." The

[1] *A Mission Record of the California Indians* (Kroeber) quotes the word as used by the San Fernando Mission Indians, apparently for the wild plum. In New Mexico it means one of the common salt-bushes of the Southwest, *Atriplex canescens*.

name *adenostoma* is a Greek word manufactured for the occasion and means gland-mouth, as meaningless as the Greek itself until you are shown some minute fleshy glands that dot the throat of the flower's calyx tube.

On a day of early December, 1846, as the ragged little army of Lieutenant Emory (you will hear of him again in our chapter on Cactus) were in the neighborhood of Warner's Pass in the southern cordillera of San Diego County, the botanists of the party collected specimens of a queer cousin of the *chamiso* to which Dr. Torrey afterward gave the name *Adenostoma sparsifolium*, the sparse-leaved, from the characteristic foliage, which is thread-like and scattered and borne mostly in tufts at the branch tips. The bark hangs in ruddy shreds and tatters from the cinnamon-colored trunk and branches, and has given rise to one of the shrub's several popular names, ribbon-wood. No less graphic is red-shank. Among the Spanish-speaking population one hears it called *Yerba del pasmo* (as we would say, convulsion weed) and both they and the Indians make of bark and foliage a lotion or tea for the cure of cramps, snake bites, miscellaneous sores, and above all lockjaw, the dreaded *pasmo real*, so likely to result from cuts by their rusty, outworn implements. The leafy twigs are boiled well and the wound washed with the liquor. After that, a piece of flannel may be laid upon the spot and steamed thoroughly over the kettle. The shrub is of more local occurrence than *chamiso*, being found only from Santa Barbara County southward.

Growing on arid foothill slopes and forming an important element in the chaparral is another rosaceous shrub or small tree with grayish, prominently veined leaves suggesting a birch's. It is *Cercocarpus betuloides*, the mountain mahogany. In the matter of blooming it is so exceedingly modest that one not botanically learned would never in the world suspect its relationship to the rose. The tiny flowers without petals are scattered along the branchlets, a mere blob of stamens and pistil filling the mouth of a tubular calyx, after the fashion of a Lilliputian ice-cream cone. So inconspicuously is the blooming done that few people ever notice the fact, but with the aging year comes a remarkable transformation. The place where pistil and stamens were is now filled by one hard seed tipped with a spirally twisted, feathery tail two or three inches long. The whole crown of the shrub is enhaloed with these airy plumelets, which shimmer entrancingly in the sun and catch the eye from afar. At maturity each seed sits loosely in its little pocket, responsive to the autumnal breeze, which neatly lifts it out and sends it drifting to its appointed goal in the scheme of things—a linnet's crop, perhaps, or the snug crevice of some sunny cliff, where by its spiral tail it bores itself a nest to sprout in. The popular name mountain mahogany has been given because of the exceeding hardness of the wood—a nail can hardly be driven into it—and also because of its mahogany red color when fresh cut. To the Indians, who were ignorant of iron until the white man came bringing it, this shrub and a kindred species, *Cercocarpus ledifolius*, met an important need in providing material for fish spears, arrow foreshafts and points, and especially digging sticks for grubbing out the bulbs and roots that entered largely into the dietary of many tribes. For this purpose a straight piece, simply pointed and hardened in the fire, was as effective as a spade bought at the trader's. I have in my possession an ancient six-foot stick evi-

Thistle or Prickly Poppy

Matilija Poppy

CREAMCUPS (*Platystemon Californicus*)

dently of mountain mahogany, pointed at one end and neatly beveled at the other, which had been used in cutting out the tender, edible buds of the mescal plant by some Diegueños of southern California. It was found cached away in a pile of boulders on the desert slope of the mountains, where it had evidently been deposited against another spring, which perhaps to the owner never came. It has the appearance of considerable age and is as hard as nails. Hard-tack is another name Californians sometimes give it, because of its hardness.

Near akin to Cercocarpus in botanical character, though not in appearance, is the small shrub *Purshia tridentata,* which will attract you, if it attracts you at all, by its stubby little fan-shaped leaves thrice notched at the top. The solitary flowers of an anemic yellow, each with a conical pistil bulging up from the center of a circle of stamens, are succeeded by small, dry, bony fruits of an intense bitterness, whence the name Bitter-brush is sometimes heard. Buck-brush and antelope-brush as vernacular names also have their adherents. Furthermore, you may hear it called greasewood. Purshia is a denizen of dry slopes and arid upland valleys from the Sierra Nevada and mountains of Oregon eastward to the Rockies, and I fancy it was among the plants brought to notice by the Lewis and Clark expedition. At any rate, it was first described along with their collections in a *Flora of North America,* written by Frederick Pursh, though he gave it another name. Many years later the botanist Nuttall renamed the plant in Pursh's honor as we now know it. In the 1820's David Douglas sent seeds of it to England, where Purshia is still occasionally grown as a curiosity, they say.

That Frederick Pursh, of whom mention will frequently be made in these discursive pages, was a memorable man in that he was the author of the second—really the first notable—account of the plants of the United States. A German by birth and well educated as a plantsman, he turned up in Philadelphia at the beginning of the nineteenth century, and from 1802 to 1805 was gardener to William Hamilton's famous estate, now known as Woodlands Cemetery. Among the friendships Pursh made at that time was that of Professor Benjamin Smith Barton, teacher of botany at the University of Pennsylvania, who became impressed with the humble gardener's knowledge and ability and undertook to finance him on a botanical trip or two into the American wilderness. His travels were not very extensive, partly owing, it is charged, to the slimness and irregularity of his patron's remittances, but he managed to become fairly well acquainted with the flora *in situ* from southern Virginia to the Great Lakes and New England. Then in 1807 we find him in charge of Dr. Hosack's famous Botanic Garden in New York City, and four or five years later behold him with his botanical baggage set down in London. There he promptly fell in with the celebrated botanist Aylmer Bourke Lambert, who had an extensive herbarium of American plants and who kept open house to visiting naturalists from all parts of the world. Under the auspices of Lambert, Pursh set about the task of producing an up-to-date North American Flora, and in the extraordinarily short space of a year and a half ("I shut him up in the house to keep him at work," Lambert used to say) he prepared and published to the world his *magnum opus, Flora Americae Septentrionalis*, which with its descriptions of about 3,000 flowering plants and ferns (much fewer than are now known to be indigenous to California alone) put the previous work on the subject quite in the shade. Half a dozen years after its publication, which was in 1814, Pursh died in obscurity in Canada at the age of forty-six. Not so long ago his grave was discovered, and some kindly Canadian naturalists had his remains removed to Montreal. There they now rest beneath a decent monument erected to his memory, where the worshiper at the shrine of notability may pay his devoirs to the memory of one who left family and country to follow all his life amid poverty, disappointment and hardship, in wilderness and in garden close, the beck of his mistress Flora. He had the reward of the pioneer, the thrill of seeing first what none had seen before, and the unction that comes of telling the world about it.

In the mountains of California, principally in the north, spreading up to Alaska and eastward to the Rockies, the shrub *Amelanchier alnifolia* whitens springtime thickets with its tattery bloom. Lewis and Clark came upon it early in their memorable expedition, and later on, the plump, purplish berries added a bit of variety to the party's monotonous fare, though to more pampered palates they are insipid enough. Because of these berries, the commonalty call the plant June-berry, from the time of ripening in some localities, though July- or August-berry would be quite as appropriate in others. Indians have always been fond of the fruit, consuming it either raw or dried. In midsummer the women with their gathering baskets and babies would repair to the rocky slopes or stream sides, where the shrub abounds, to harvest the berries, which would then be spread on mats or flat rocks in the sun to dry. According to Lewis

and Clark's narrative, the Columbia River Indians
made a sort of bread by pounding up the dried berries
and baking the mass in large loaves, weighing ten to
fifteen pounds apiece. In this way the juiciness was
better retained. Broken up and soaked in water, these
loaves made a savory dish for winter consumption. A
vernacular name for Amelanchier that shares popularity
with June-berry is service-berry—a term that has given
philologists much exercise of wit. Unlike June-berry,
which is of American origin, service-berry comes from
Europe, and would seem to be a case of name transference. Dr. R. C. A. Prior, in his classic work *Popular
Names of British Plants,* records the term as applied to
a poor sort of wild pear common in Europe (*Sorbus
domestica*) and used from ancient times for making a
fermented drink. He derives it from the Latin *cervisia,*
a word used by Pliny for "beer." It has always been customary for newcomers in America to apply Old World
names to plants that reminded them in some way of
plants they knew at home, and this may well have been
the case with service-berry. At any rate, it serves to
hang an argument upon.

Far more widely known in California than the June-
berry is that handsome shrub the Christmas-berry or
Toyon, currently misnamed California holly, for holly
it is not, the *Photinia arbutifolia* of the botanists. Its
first appearance in history appears to have been on a
November day in 1792, when Archibald Menzies, herb-
orizing in the vicinity of what came to be San Francisco,
happened upon an ornamental evergreen shrub "plentifully cropped with red berries," which he guessed might
be a new species of *Crataegus* or hawthorn. He succeeded
in introducing it into cultivation in Great Britain, where

it has been sparingly grown ever since under the common name California maybush, "may" being an English synonym for the hawthorn. In its native California —and it is native nowhere except in California, if in that term we include the peninsula of Lower California—it all but equals the California poppy in the popular affections. The clustered red berries and clean foliage make an excellent substitute for real holly at Christmas time, at which season people troop to the hills for the berry-laden branches for use in home decoration, and street stands are gay with the cheerful color. A few years ago a wave of apprehension swept the state lest wholesale gathering by a rapidly increasing population would exterminate the plant, and a law was passed prohibiting its collection on state lands or on private property without the owner's written permission. Nevertheless, pruning of the bushes, if done with discretion and with knife or clippers, is more of a benefit than a detriment, a fact appreciated by the guardians of the national forests, who customarily allow the public to gather for private use if the bush is not mutilated. The raw berries, which are rather acid, are edible in a way, as might reasonably be expected of a member of the family that includes the apple, peach and plum, and the Indians consumed them extensively, both raw and cooked. The berries would be tossed about in a basket with hot pebbles or wood-coals, the ordinary aboriginal way of roasting seeds and berries. The Spanish Californians, too, had a gastronomic interest in them. One method of preparation which I have from a Santa Barbara lady was to put the berries in hot water, strain through a colander, then wrap in a hot cloth, and after half an hour they were ready to serve.

Another tells me her family's custom was to boil the
berries for two minutes, then pour them into the bottom
of a clean, warmed, empty flour sack, and lap the
upper part of the sack over the berry-filled bottom
"turnoverwise." Then all would be wrapped about with
warmed cloths and set on a sunny table or window seat
for an hour or two. (You will recognize in this the principle of the fireless cooker.) Still another *anciana*, a bit
more sybaritic in her tastes, would put the raw berries
in a bag, sprinkle with sugar, then place the bag and
all in a slow oven, and serve (as she remarked) *poco
tiempo*, that is, after a while! Obviously, toyon pudding
à la californienne is something a modern chef might
find worth his art. Furthermore, the berries are capable
of yielding an agreeable cider, as both *Californios* and
Indians long ago knew. On the California islands the
berries grow especially bright and plump, and there is a
form with fruit of a rich yellow color. Millspaugh and
Nuttall in their recent *Flora of Santa Catalina Island*
state that the fishermen there have used the bark for
tanning their nets and sails.

It is interesting, I think, to know that Hollywood,
Los Angeles's most famous quarter, owes its name to
this shrub. A half century or so ago one Horace Henderson Wilcox, looking for a chance to turn an honest
penny, purchased a considerable acreage of ranch land
in that region, subdivided it, and offered it to the public
in small parcels. At that time the hills roundabout
abounded in California holly, so that the name Hollywood naturally enough suggested itself for the pretty
little town that eventually came into being there and
was for many years an independent municipality.[1]

[1]L. and V. S. Bartlett: *Los Angeles in 7 Days*, p. 81.

Also associated with Christmas in California is the holly-leaf cherry, *Prunus ilicifolia*. Its glossy, spiny-toothed leaves so well simulate those of the real holly that they are utilized by the makers of holiday wreaths, combined with the berries of the Photinia. This cherry is a denizen of chaparral slopes as well as valley lands from San Francisco Bay to Lower California, and its dark crimson "cherries," three quarters of an inch or so in diameter and ripe in the autumn, were another cherished food of the Indians. You yourself will enjoy nibbling at them when fully ripe, for the sake of the sweet thin pulp, but in throwing away the great seed you will be discarding what to the Indian was the fruit's especial treasure. With that strange insight into the hidden worth of the apparently worthless fruits of the wilderness, the Indian discovered that by cracking the stony pit he—or rather she, for this was woman's work—released a kernel unpalatable, indeed, but full of nutrition. These kernels dried and roasted were ground on a stone mortar and the meal subjected to successive leachings with water, as in the case of the acorn. A gruel made of this leached meal was a favorite dish among the Californian aborigines, who called the shrub *islay*, as did the Spanish people after them. On Santa Catalina and other California islands there occurs a variety with ample, spineless leaves. It not infrequently attains a height of forty feet or more, a tree of great beauty, and is common in cultivation under the name of Catalina cherry.

The little roses of the Potentilla in clusters of yellow or white and half a hundred species greet the rambler in California and Oregon whether on mountain, plain or seacoast. Most famous of all is *Potentilla anserina*, a north temperate species of wide distribution, occurring in the United States on both coasts and as far north as Alaska and Greenland, as well as in Europe and Asia. It revels in the moisture of stream banks and marshy places, its long-stalked golden flowers lifted well above a basal tuft of tansy-like leaves. These are silvery white on the under surface (or on both surfaces in the variety *argentea*) whence it is most appropriately called silverweed. A feature not always realized is hidden in the ground—the bundled roots, which are edible. Reginald Farrer, in his delightful book *The Rainbow Bridge*, tells of being presented in Tibet with "bowls of Silverweed tubers, little nutty things so delicious (like young asparagus or new potatoes) as to make one feel that one's greed need never flag in England so long as *Potentilla anserina* abounds by every wayside—one of our loveliest and most odious of weeds." It is quite capable of becoming a nuisance, for it spreads mightily by creeping, rooting runners. Among the score of vernacular names by which it goes in England is Goose-tansy, because, according to an old herbalist, it is eaten by geese, an explanation to which one authority on English plant names takes exception, preferring to think that the name merely implies that only a goose would take it for tansy! And yet that qualifying *anserina* (pertaining to geese), gravely given by Linnæus, could hardly have so cynical a basis, one would think. It seems strange that the California aborigines with their flair for detecting hidden economic worth in the wild plants should not have learned of the silverweed's edible roots, but I do not find that they did.

CHAPTER III

*Of Lewis and Clark and Their Namesakes among
the Pacific Coast Flowers.*

THERE is a tradition that in a little shop devoted to
Flora and Ceres on Market Street near Second in
Philadelphia, the idea was hatched of that transcontinental trip to the Pacific coast, which developed into
the historic Lewis and Clark expedition of 1804–06,
and brought to light, among other matters, many interesting plants of the Pacific slope. The little shop in
question was the seed and nursery goods establishment
of Bernard M'Mahon, an expatriated young Irishman
of liberal political views, who settled in Philadelphia
about the year 1796. He was a man of remarkable personality, a friend of Thomas Jefferson and other notables of the time, and an enthusiastic plant lover, so that
his shop became a favorite rendezvous for botanical
people and plant amateurs, attracted thither to discuss
the news of the floral world and horticultural problems.
It is known that, upon the return of the explorers, it
was M'Mahon who was largely responsible for introducing into the gardens of America and Europe many choice
flowers whose seeds were gathered on the journey.
Thomas Nuttall, one of the habitués of the M'Mahon
shop—a botanist of whom we shall hear more in the
progress of this book—has preserved his memory in the

25

genus Mahonia, the evergreen barberries of the Pacific coast.[1]

Although the route of the Lewis and Clark expedition lay outside of California, a number of the plants discovered include California in their range, and bear names that commemorate one or the other of the two leaders. Among these is the remarkable bitter-root, *Lewisia rediviva*, dedicated to Captain Meriwether Lewis of the memorable partnership. It occurs from the Rockies westward to British Columbia, and south in the mountains as far as the southern California ranges. The first description of the plant was published in 1814 in Pursh's *North American Flora*. The specimen had been collected on the Lou-Lou fork of the Bitter-root River in Montana, and Pursh noticed when he came to prepare a description from the dried material, that although it had been in the herbarium for several years, the roots still showed signs of life. Out of curiosity, he planted them, and, marvelously enough, they revived and began to grow, which gave him the idea of the specific name *rediviva*, "that lives again." Incredible as that story sounds, Sir William Hooker, director of the Royal Botanic Gardens at Kew, had even a more remarkable experience half a century later. He planted a Lewisia root that a year and a half before had been immersed in boiling water to kill it for herbarium purposes, and yet, in spite of that fervent bath and the passage of time, it produced when planted out perfect flowers of great beauty, a picture of which anyone may see by reference to Curtis's *Botanical Magazine*, plate 5395.

Lewisia has long been used as a rock-garden subject,

[1]Bailey: *New Cyclopedia of American Horticulture*, art. M'Mahon.

having been introduced into England in 1826. It has a taste for sunny crevices, but after a liberal display of its superb flowers, it enjoys fooling the novice by shriveling up completely and looking for months as dead as a door nail. At the best the plant is the veriest dwarf, barely two inches high, often less than one inch, with flat little fat leaves an inch or so in length, in the midst of which are borne the showy, many-petaled rose-purple or white flowers. Under favorable conditions these are the size of a silver dollar and are as charming in their way as are the blossoms of Lewisia's relative, the beloved Portulaca, and, like these, expand only in the sunshine. From a practical standpoint the plant was of great economic importance to the Northwestern Indians, who in their necessity discovered that the bitter parsnip-shaped roots possess a nutritious heart of starch, which cooking reduces to a pasty mass, palatable, at least, to Indian taste. Since the roots are not large, to gather them in quantity is quite a task, and there is a tradition that a sackful used to be considered equal to the price of a horse. The statement is not very illuminating, as sacks, like pieces of chalk, vary in size, and horses in worthwhileness.

The explorers first came upon Lewisia among the Shoshones in western Montana, and understanding the Indians to call it *spatlum*, they so labeled the specimens that they carried home. This seems, however, to have been a misapplication of the word, which philologists say really means tobacco. The obvious thing for Americans to call a plant of so bitter a root was just bitter-root, and as that it is still universally known on the Pacific slope. The state of Montana has taken the beautiful flower to her heart and made it her floral emblem, while a mountain chain, a river and a valley contribute to the perpetuation of the vernacular name.

Also commemorative of Captain Lewis is another floral aristocrat, the western mock orange or syringa, the shrub *Philadelphus Lewisii*, which, too, was given its name by Pursh. Its deliciously fragrant white flowers and general similarity of appearance to the garden mock-orange (an Old World species) make it easily identifiable. It occurs from Montana through Idaho to British Columbia, and thence south in the foothills and lower altitudes of the mountains to southern California. It, too, has the distinction of being an official state flower, having been so elected a number of years ago by Idaho. In California the shrub varies slightly from the typical form farther north, and careful botanists have eased their consciences by describing two forms or varieties, *californicus* and *gordonianus* respectively. The straight young shoots, very light of weight because of their abundant pith, were prized by certain of the California Indians for arrow shafts, a sharpened point made of some hardwood, such as oak, mountain mahogany or dogwood, being inserted in the tip of the shaft. To the mothers of the tribe these shoots of the syringa had a softer appeal. They were excellent, it was found, for the making of cradles to carry babies in.[1] Among the Karuk Indians of northwestern California the syringa was a favorite wood for the making of tobacco pipes. Such pipes were about six inches long and shaped much like a white man's cigar holder—the broader end serving as the bowl. The smoker, when inhaling, tipped the pipe up and his head

[1] V. K. Chesnut in *Plants Used by the Indians of Mendocino County.*

back. Mr. J. P. Harrington, in his delightful monograph *Tobacco among the Karuk Indians of California*,[1] describes in detail the making of a pipe from a syringa stem, as told him by an Indian. One method of boring the hole in the stem for the smoke to pass through is curious enough to mention: The grub of a certain beetle would be imprisoned in the pith at one end of the stem and left to eat its way through to the other. A case of the use of the aboriginal head to save manual labor!

Yet another floral compliment that Lewis had at Pursh's hands was the bestowal of his name on a new species of wild flax, which attracted the explorers' attention day after day near the Continental Divide, and especially interested them because of its having a perennial root. As it proved to be new to science, Pursh called it *Linum Lewisii*, and so do we to this day. Its fleeting blue flowers, sometimes an inch across, beautifully dye for an hour many a high mountain glade from southern California to British Columbia, whence it drifts eastward to the Great Plains. Frémont records finding it in the Rocky Mountain foothills, growing "as in a sown field." While the fiber in its stems is less tough than that of the flax of commerce, it is still very strong, and served the aborigines in good stead for their stringage and cordage. And then there is Lewis's Mimulus (*M. Lewisii*), a particularly lovely thing with generally pink to rose-red corollas on long pedicels, frequent on stream borders and moist ground from the Sierra Nevada northward and eastward. Every summer its colorful colonies delight visitors to our northwestern national parks—Yosemite, Mount Rainier and Glacier.

Not to be partial, Pursh named another pretty flower

[1] *Bureau of American Ethnology*, Bulletin 94.

for the other partner in the expedition, dedicating to
Captain Clark the genus Clarkia. This was founded on
a plant collected by these explorers on the Kooskooskie
River in northern Idaho, and to it Pursh gave the name
Clarkia pulchella, that is, the beautiful. It is a rather
low-growing annual, bearing in summer slender racemes
of showy lilac or rose flowers with quaint thrice-lobed
petals. For twenty years it remained unknown to the
civilized world except as a dried specimen in a herbarium, and then David Douglas rediscovered it near the
Great Falls of the Columbia in Oregon and sent seeds
of it to England, where it was speedily introduced into
cultivation. Though abundant enough on prairies and
plains from Montana through northeastern Oregon to
British Columbia, it has so far not been found indigenous in California, if we except one doubtful report.
California, however, is rich enough in other species of
Clarkia, having at least six good ones. Of these Douglas
was the discoverer of two, *Clarkia elegans* and *C. rhom-
boidea*, and thanks to him Europe was growing them
in its gardens in the early 1830's. Indeed, Clarkias as
garden flowers sprang into instant popularity abroad,
once they were offered—an eminence which they have
not yet lost. Seven years after Douglas sent home the
seeds of *Clarkia pulchella*, the English botanist Lindley
wrote: "The name Clarkia, like the name Rose, carries
a charm with it that beautifies even a weed, for it is
impossible not to associate it with the idea of that sweet
North American flower that in a few short years has
changed from an obscure botanical rarity to the ornament of every flower market from London and Paris
to Moscow and Stockholm." Under cultivation Clarkia
has developed great variation, and numerous forms are

offered by dealers today, some of them double, while in color they range all the way from white through salmon pink and the magentas to deep purple. *Clarkia concinna*, a denizen of wooded slopes in the coast ranges, is less well known than are the three species above mentioned. It is a charming flower, suggesting *C. pulchella* in the deep coloring of its pink petals, and seems to have come to the world's notice by way of St. Petersburg. Between 1820 and 1841, the Russian American Fur Company had stations near the mouth of the Russian River in what is now Sonoma County, and from time to time seeds and botanical specimens were sent thence to the St. Petersburg Imperial Botanic Gardens. In this way, numerous California species were first described and named, among them, this Clarkian beauty.

The total number of specimens brought home by Lewis and Clark was not great—only about 150, all obtained on the homeward journey, those collected when the party was westbound having met with mishap and irretrievable loss—a sort of tragedy that frequently befell the scientific labor of those early times in the western wilderness. Lewis, who was a member of the American Philosophical Society of Philadelphia (an organization, by the way, of which Thomas Jefferson, sponsor of the expedition, was for many years president), seems to have done most of the collecting. Upon the party's return he turned the botanical spoil over to the society, which placed it in the hands of Dr. Benjamin S. Barton, eminent in that day as a naturalist, and he in turn passed it along to Pursh, to the enrichment thereby of the latter's *Flora of North America*, which was published in England eight years later, and of which we heard in the last chapter.

CHAPTER IV

Lilies by Other Names; the Story of Camassia and How It Led to a War; of James Brodie's Flower and the Mariposa-tulip; and Kindred Matters.

DESCENDING the western slope of the Bitter-root Mountains one September day of 1805, the Lewis and Clark expedition came to a beautiful open plain where there was an encampment of Nez Percé Indians, who hospitably set before the travelers a rustic repast of buffalo meat, dried salmon, some berries and an assortment of roots. Among the last was one round like an onion and sweetish of taste, and from that day on it is frequently mentioned in the journal under a number of spellings, as quamash, quawmash, quamas, kamash, kamas, commis or commes. The following June, upon the return journey, the expedition camped at the same spot, now known as Weippe Valley in northern Idaho, "on the bank of a small stream," so runs the diary, "in a point of woods bordering the extensive, level and beautiful prairie which is intersected by several rivulets, and which, as the quamash is now in blossom, presents a perfect resemblance of lakes of clear water." It was one of many such meadows that formerly gemmed our northwest, where the Indians would camp to dig the bulbs, which formed an important part of their food supply, or to break their journeys from place to place. The plant ranges southward to central California.

Photo by L. E. Martindale

GREASEWOOD (*Adenostoma fasciculatum*)

The Country of the RED SHANK, *Yerba del Pasmo*, in the Santa Rosa Mountains, California. (*Adenostoma sparsifolium*)

Perhaps you have seen it in the Yosemite, or even in gardens, for zealous amateurs of liliaceous bulbous plants find joy in cultivating it for the sake of the splendid blue flowers. In the language of the botanists it is Camassia.

Camas is the form of the name that has superseded the others of Lewis and Clark's journal, and according to Professor A. L. Kroeber of the University of California, reaches us through the Chinook jargon and signifies "sweet." It rather plentifully spots the maps of today, being attached to villages, creeks, valleys and prairies. The bulb, especially that of the species *Camassia quamash*, was one of the most important foods of the Indians of the regions where it grew, and was eaten either raw, boiled into a kind of soup, or baked into a cake.

One fertile source of irritation on the part of the aborigines toward the interloping white settlers was the latter's cavalier encroachment upon the red man's immemorial camas meadows. Indian rights in these were sometimes officially recognized by the United States government in its treaties, but pioneers three thousand miles from Washington rarely bothered their heads with such legal niceties, contenting themselves with the nine points of the law that possession gave. In the late 1870's some half-starved Bannocks, coming down to Big Camas Prairie to fill their empty stomachs, found settlers' droves of hogs rooting up and eating the precious bulbs by wholesale, whereupon the Indians in exasperation shot the herders, and so was started an uprising that required a lot of soldiers, money and several months of time to quell.

Camassia Leichtlinii, commemorating in its name a

noted plantsman of the last century, Max Leichtlin of Carlsruhe, occurs on grassy plains and wet flats of northern California. It is of similar appearance and use to *C. quamash*, though the flowers are frequently creamy white. If you have not entirely outgrown the child within you, you will be interested in the withering flower, which twists itself over the seed vessel "like a bon-bon," to quote Dr. Jepson's neat simile, remaining so until ready to drop.

Great care must be exercised in the gathering of camas bulbs to avoid those of the very similar looking *Zygadenus venenosus,* which sometimes grows with camas. When in flower the zygadene may be distinguished by its small, greenish-white blossoms. The bulbs are extremely poisonous to man and on this account are popularly called death camas; but pigs, they say, thrive on both sorts indifferently. Famous as the true camas is for human consumption, the tenderfoot does well to be temperate in its use, for in excess it is apt to be both emetic and purgative. The Lewis and Clark journals contain more than one entry recording the dolorous effects of a root diet on white digestions not accustomed to it.

Another of those explorers' interesting discoveries among the Lily tribe was made while they were in winter quarters at Fort Clatsop at the mouth of the Columbia. The Indians thereabout used a novel sort of basket, in shape like a truncated cone and woven so closely as to be watertight. Such baskets served the double purpose of hat and bucket, and were made of cedar bark and the grass-like leaves of a plant, very strong and pliant. The journal calls it bear-grass, and specimens of the living plant were collected on the return through Idaho. On the strength of these, the plant received the name *Xerophyllum tenax,* "the dry leaf that holds fast."

It ranges from Yellowstone and Glacier national parks northwestward to British Columbia and south to central California, affecting dry ridges and borders of mountain meadows in open coniferous forests, where its sociable gatherings, often acres in extent, crowned with masses of white bloom, make a spectacular sight. In favorable situations the plants grow so thickly together as to form solid mats, so slippery as to make walking upon them all but impossible. An individual plant must be several years old before it is ready to bloom. Then from a tuft of leafage it shoots upward a stout, shaggy shaft that develops a dense club-shaped raceme of fragrant white flowers, making up in numbers what they lack in size.

David Douglas recognized the value of the bear-grass for cultivated grounds even when out of flower, and introduced it into English gardens, where it still has some place. Its interest to our Pacific coast country folk is attested by a host of vernacular names, some cryptic enough to prove an interesting puzzle. Thus there are pine-lily, fire-lily, elk-grass, squaw-grass, turkey-beard, soap-grass, as well as the more usual bear-grass. The reason for this last name, while easy to guess at, has not been so easy to make sure of. My quest for it eventually took me to Mr. Leslie L. Haskin, of Brownsville, Oregon, an industrious student of native plants. He was given the following explanation by an experienced trapper and woodsman:

In the spring, when the bears first come out of their winter sleep, it seems they seek the higher sunny ridges where the snow has melted away and the bear-grass grows, and digging up the tuberous rootstocks they eat them with apparent relish. The same woodsman further said that the roots boiled and the water evaporated make an excellent soap, which would account for the name soap-grass. Roasting dissipates the saponaceous quality and renders the root edible, at least to Indians.

More popular in the aboriginal dietary were the bulbous corms of two of California's most characteristic groups of wild flowers—Brodiaea and Calochortus. Lifting them from their earthy beds with sharp-pointed digging sticks of oak or mountain mahogany, the Indians consumed the nutty morsels either raw or cooked— the cooking being done in a fireless-cooker sort of way. A pit was dug, lined with heated rocks, the bulbs placed in layers separated by green leaves, the whole covered with earth and a fire then lighted on top. After a day or two the pit was opened and the well steamed roots were ripe for eating, the sweeter for the long, slow cooking. They were considered best when gathered soon after the flowers had fallen. Both harvesting and cooking were usually done by several families in company, and in the old days with song and ceremony. But now, no longer. The young Indians ape white fashions and know little or nothing of the ways of their fathers.

The first Brodiaea seen by any botanist seems to have been the so-called Harvest Brodiaea, whose erect, violet-purple funnels of bloom are abundant about the time of the hay harvest throughout the Great Central Valley of California, as well as on the Sierra and Coast Range foothills. Southward it is found sparingly nearly to the Mexican border, and northward as far as western British Columbia. It was collected in 1792 by Archibald

Menzies, botanist of the Vancouver expedition, which made stops on the Pacific coast on the way around the world. A generation later the indefatigable Douglas sent bulbs from Oregon to England, where it bloomed in 1828, and is cherished to this day by English amateurs.

The name *Brodiaea grandiflora* was given it in 1811 by the eminent British botanist J. E. Smith in honor of his "wealthy friend and patron" the Scot James Brodie of Brodie House, Elgin. And thereby hangs a tale. It appears that the plant had been described and named a few years before as *Hookera coronaria* by Richard Anthony Salisbury in his work entitled *Paradisus Londoniensis*, an account of plants grown in the vicinity of London, the name *Hookera* commemorating the artist William Hooker, who did the illustrations. Now, if you think professional botanists are like billing doves in a nest, let this little tale disillusion you, for Salisbury and Smith got into a furious quarrel, which resulted in Smith's calling Salisbury names and conspiring with the principal botanical moguls of the time to ignore Salisbury's work ever after. As matters now stand with our pretty flower, some botanists still hold with Salisbury while others divide the honors between him and Smith, accepting the latter's generic name and the former's specific, that is, *Brodiaea coronaria*.

Abundant as the Harvest Brodiaea is, there is another Brodiaea even more so, *B. capitata*, widely distributed in valleys and on hillsides from the Mexican line to southern Oregon. Everybody knows its plump clusters of smallish blue flowers topping a slender stalk in the lush grasses of the rainy season. Its sure place in the affections of the people is witnessed by a multitude of common names, as California hyacinth, cluster-lily, grass-nuts, wild onion, blue-dicks, Spanish-lily, and just Brodiaea, usually mispronounced by dropping the *i*. In addition to these Dr. Jepson records nigger-toes, nigger-babies, sugar-lump and Indian-lily. Among Spanish-speaking Californians the plant is called *caco-mite*, one of those interesting survivals of the Aztec speech of which so many still linger in odd corners of the country. *Cacomitl*, they say, was the word as Montezuma spoke it, and was translated by one of the old Spanish chroniclers as "certain roots with the flavor of chestnuts." It was especially the name for the bulbs of *Tigridia pavonia*, the exquisite tiger-flower of our gardens, native to Mexico and used by the ancients there as an article of diet. Brought to California by the early Spaniards, the word came to be used for the edible corms of our *Brodiaea capitata*.

My friend Doña Matilde, who loves to talk of the old ways, informs me that when she was a girl the spring held no greater joy for the children than going *cacomite* hunting; but now it is different; they have candy and chewing gum and "pop," and their tastes have been weaned from the simplicities of nature.

The botanical history of this charming flower dates from its discovery in 1847 or thereabouts near Monterey by Karl Theodor Hartweg, a sturdy young German plantsman who was sent to Mexico in 1836 by the Horticultural Society of London to collect plants and seeds for English gardens. After several years spent in Spanish America he proceeded to California, where, although much hampered in his movements by the unsettled state of the country at the time, he succeeded in making many collections new to science, among them this favorite wilding.

Though the flowers of most species of Brodiaea are blue or purplish, there are also yellow species, and a very remarkable one in scarlet. This last is *Brodiaea Ida-maia*, which sends up in spring a slender stem, sometimes as much as three feet tall, bearing at the summit a loose cluster of pendulous tubular flowers, scarlet with a green tip. These so much resemble a bunch of fire-crackers that the popular name Fire-cracker-plant was inevitable.

It is native to open woods from the San Francisco Bay region to the Siskiyous and southern Oregon, and the story of its discovery has been preserved to us. One spring day in 1867 Dr. Alphonso Wood, a New Yorker, and author of many popular books on botany, was traveling by stage through the Trinity Mountains of California when the driver pointed to this flower growing by the way and said that he liked it so much that he always called it Ida May, after his little daughter of that name. Wood saw that the plant was something new, and having a normal taste for human sentiment as well as for the strict facts of science, he published a description of it under the name *Brevoortia Ida-maia*—the first part to honor one J. Carson Brevoort, a patron of science of his acquaintance, and the latter part to commemorate the parental affection of the stage driver for his child; furthermore, because it was the ides (15th) of May when the flower was discovered.[1] Time has caused the name Brevoortia to be discarded

[1] Thomas Meehan: *The Native Flowers and Ferns of U.S.*, 2 ser. ii: 38.

by many botanists for Brodiaea, but Ida-maia still sticks
and keeps alive the memory of the little Trinity Mountain lass whose father loved the flower that reminded
him of her. It has been introduced into gardens both
here and abroad, and I have seen it listed in an English
publication as vegetable fire-cracker!

And here as well as anywhere something may be said
about the miscalled dog's-tooth violets—species of the
genus *Erythronium*, of which the Pacific coast has nine
or ten indigenous sorts, among the loveliest of the Lily
family. Over a century ago David Douglas had introduced into England at least one species, the golden-
flowered *E. grandiflorum*, which Lewis and Clark had
found before him. This is the species that sheets with
color the alpine meadows and fringes the midsummer
snow banks of Glacier National Park, where it has
acquired the common name glacier lily. It or its variety
parviflorum follows the high mountains to the Pacific
and then northward into British Columbia. Mr. Stand-
ley, in his *Flora of Glacier National Park*, states that
the bulbs are eaten by bears, which at high altitudes in
the park plough up the sod in their search for them.

Even better known, perhaps, is the white-flowered
Erythronium montanum, common in alpine meadows
of the Oregon and Washington mountains, and especially noted in Mount Rainier National Park, where
every summer visitors are ravished by the luxuriant
growth of these marvelous flowers. "Avalanche lilies,"
they call them, presumably from their being often found
at the very edge of snow fields. The inventive genius
of Erythronium lovers, by the way, has been sorely
taxed to find a suitable vernacular name for the group.
Oregon children settled long ago on "lamb's tongue,"

and in Utah, I am told, "Easter bells" has its devotees. Eastern people cling rather stubbornly to "dog's-tooth violet," though a revolt against this term, started a number of years ago by John Burroughs and still going, would substitute "fawn lily," from the leaves of the common Eastern species being prettily dappled like the skin of a fawn. "Trout lily," too, has its advocates, from the contemporaneous blooming of the flower and the opening of the fishing season.

"Dog's-tooth violet," however, is not so senseless as it would seem. It has a history that carries us back to the day of Papa Linnæus. There is in Europe a species to which Linnæus gave the name *Erythronium dens-canis*—*Erythronium* from the Greek for "red," the color of the flower in that species, and *dens-canis* (dog's tooth), because the oblong white bulbs resembled dog's teeth. But that, you will say, does not explain the violet in the name. Upon that Prior in his *Popular Names of British Plants* throws light. According to that authoritative delver into the past, the word "violet" was formerly not restricted to the botanical genus *viola*, but was extended by ancient writers to many other plants, of diverse sorts, especially scented ones. So it is conceivable how "dog's-tooth violet" would get into the common speech of England and naturally enough be affixed to the American cousins as well.

In Chesnut's *Plants Used by the Indians of Mendocino County* a curious use of a magnificent yellow-flowered species, which he calls *giganteum*, is recorded as prevailing among the Wailakis of northern California. These Indians, it seems, cherish the belief that if they wash themselves with a decoction of the bulbs they can hinder a rattlesnake from having dreams; and as a dreaming rattlesnake, in their philosophy, is a dangerous neighbor, the plant is commandeered as preventive medicine.

Of all the Lily's western cousins none, in general esteem, excels in beauty the various species of Calochortus, the mariposa-tulips or -lilies. These exquisite creations, whose popular name mariposa, the Spanish for butterfly, is due to the versicolored spots and blotches and pencilings of the corolla in most species, are native almost entirely to the Pacific slope, California being particularly rich in them.

Like all Gaul, the genus is divisible into three sections: Typical mariposas, with generous, bowl-like corollas poised high on slender stems; the star-tulips, lowly beauties with smallish, wide-open corollas fringed and hairy-crested within; and the globe-tulips or fairy-lanterns, with nodding globular flowers in yellow, rose or white. Among the last is *Calochortus albus*, the white one, which John Muir thought "the very loveliest of all the Lily family—a spotless soul, plant saint, that everyone must love and so be made the better. It puts the wildest mountaineer on his good behavior. With this plant the whole world would seem rich, though none other existed."

The first Calochortus to be noted under that name in the annals of science is a native of Washington, thence eastward to Montana. It was collected by Lewis and Clark on the headwaters of the Kooskooskie River in Idaho, and although by no means as beautiful as many others of the genus, the charm of the little withered flower with its grass-like leaves brought back for Frederick Pursh to classify was so evident that he gave it a name to match, *Calochortus elegans*, or as one would say in English, the elegant pretty-grass. But the man who really made the world acquainted with the mariposa-tulips and their value for gardens was David Douglas. He discovered and introduced into England a number of choice species, among them one that struck him as so surpassingly beautiful that he gave it the name *venustus*, that is, "outvenusing Venus"!

More recently a specialist in introducing Calochortus and other bulbous plants of the Pacific coast into gardens both at home and abroad is Mr. Carl Purdy, whose nursery, "The Terraces," near Ukiah, California, is, I fancy, the only one of its kind in point of situation. It occupies a rich little valley on the brow of a high hill —it would be called a mountain in the East—watered by a lively brook which courses through the midst of the nursery, and finally cascades down over a series of four broad limestone terraces to a valley below.

As in the case of Brodiaea, the Indians' notion with respect to Calochortus was that it was a gift of the gods to be eaten, and throughout the range of the plants the bulbs were among the most desired of foods. And not Indians alone profited by these subterranean stores of starch. One species in particular, *Calochortus Nuttallii*, has a notable history in this respect. It is indigenous to dry mountain slopes and valleys of the Sierra Nevada in California eastward to the Rocky Mountains. When the Mormons came pioneering into the Salt Lake Valley in the late 1840's, and for some years later, until their gardens became productive, they were often reduced to great straits for a bare existence, living at times upon such wild provender as the Indians taught them was edible. In this rough fare the bulbs of this lovely Calochortus formed an important element, spiced with roasted grasshoppers and washed down with mountain water. The plant is commonly called sego-lily, from the Indian name, and has in recent years been adopted as the floral emblem of the state of Utah. The scientific name of the species was given in honor of the original discoverer, Thomas Nuttall, who accompanied the Wyeth expedition to the Pacific in 1834, and of whom more in another chapter.

While these mariposas, Brodiaeas, dog-tooth violets and the rest may be truthfully enough regarded as lilies masquerading under other names (for they are all of the same family), there are some flowers popularly called lilies that have no title whatever to this name. Among these are the water lilies or Nymphaeas, whose relationship to the true lily is as far removed as is Dan from Beersheba.

Only one Nymphaea is indigenous to the Pacific coast—*N. polysepala,* nymph of many sepals, there being sometimes as many as ten of these calyx divisions. This is the common yellow pond lily, whose golden goblets of bloom, held upright on slender stems above the crowded leaves, brighten the surface of marshes and shallow lakes from the Yosemite to the coast and northward to Oregon. It is famous for having yielded certain Indian tribes—notably the Klamath—one of their characteristic and most nutritious foods, which they call *wokas.* In summer, when the seeds are ripening, the old women of the tribe, so Dr. Coville has recorded, would repair to the *wokas* swamps, and pushing off in canoes among the lily pads they would harvest the seed vessels in great quantities. The seeds were then extracted and roasted, either by tossing about in a basket with live coals or, as is customary nowadays, in a frying pan over a fire. They were then eaten dry like pop corn, which they somewhat resemble in taste, or were ground into meal on a stone slab with a peculiar squat pestle or muller having two short, diverging horns for a handle. A Klamath housewife could achieve almost as many varieties of *wokas* bread, depending largely upon the degree of ripeness of the seeds,[1] as a southern Negro cook can make of corn bread.

[1]A. L. Kroeber: *Handbook of Indians of California*, pp. 324–325.

CHAPTER V

Of the Joshua Tree; How a Newspaper Was Printed from It; and How the Indians Made a Vegetable of the Lord's Candle.

THE first historical mention of that most unlily-like of the Lily tribe—the gaunt, bayonet-leaved Joshua tree of the Mohave Desert—would appear to be in a diary left by Captain Pedro Fages, military commandant of Upper California in the early years of the Spanish occupation. In pursuit of some deserters in 1772 Fages, coming up from San Diego, traversed that western arm of the Mohave which is now called Antelope Valley, and for most of twenty-five leagues, he states, his party passed through groves of strange trees, which for want of a better name, for he was no botanist, he set down in his diary as date palms.

In 1844, Frémont's motley caravan, coming down from the north, crossed the Antelope Valley by much the same course as Fages had followed but in the opposite direction, and the fantastic creations got mention from Frémont under their right name. "Yucca trees," he says of them, "which gave a strange and southern character to the country, and suited well with the dry and desert region we were approaching. Associated with the idea of barren sands, their stiff and ungraceful form makes them to the traveler the most repulsive tree in the vegetable kingdom."

Ten years later, Dr. J. M. Bigelow, botanist of the Whipple Exploring Expedition of 1853–1854 to survey a practicable railroad route to the Pacific, recorded the finding of them along the Mohave River, whole forests of them, called palm by the Mexicans, as Fages before had done.

In the absence of adequate specimens it was not until fourteen years later that botanists determined their exact status in the vegetable kingdom, when Clarence King's expedition secured better specimens, on the strength of which Dr. Engelmann gave the tree the name by which it is now usually called—*Yucca brevifolia*, that is, the short-leaved.

All this time, however, no botanist had seen the flowers; they were collected by that Dr. C. C. Parry whose name is connected with a host of California plants. He found them—creamy white and malodorous—in southern Utah in 1874, and at last a complete description of the species was possible.

In California the Joshua tree is wholly confined to the arid wastes of the Mohave Desert, whence it spreads to northwestern Arizona, Nevada and southern Utah. A young tree is a single, wickedly bristling stem, which after a few years forks at the tip, then forks and forks again, until old specimens present intricately branched crowns, twenty or even thirty feet high, the limbs bearing green leaves only at the extreme ends. With increasing years the lower leaves die and fall away, leaving a rough checkered bark on trunk and older limbs. The extensive forests of this grotesque tree patching the desert challenged Yankee utilitarianism soon after their existence became known. The soft fibrous wood was useless for lumber, though the trunks could be employed to some extent in the making of corrals and rude buildings. Neither was it of any value as fuel, for only the dead, clinging leaves would burn. At last someone thought of it as possible paper stock. At one time, now fifty years or so ago, a small pulp mill was built at Ravenna in the Soledad Pass, about sixty miles north of Los Angeles, and paper manufactured of the trunks was shipped to various parts of this country as well as to England. A few editions of the London *Daily Telegraph* are said to have been printed on it.[1] The cost of manufacture, however, was high, and the quality left much to be desired, so the experiment was abandoned. In more recent years a less intellectual but on the whole more worth-while use for the wood has been discovered in the manufacture of surgeons' splints and artificial limbs, and many a victim of the World War has cause to bless the uncouth tree.

With the Panamint Indians, whose home was on the confines of Death Valley, the young flower buds were an article of diet. These buds develop at the branch tips, protected by a rosette of stiff leaves like a bizarre sort of cauliflower. Dr. F. V. Coville has recorded that the Indians would grasp the leaves, draw them over the bud, and with a twist and quick sidewise bend snap off the branch end. The leaves would then be discarded, and the juicy bud, which is sugary and nutritious, would be roasted on hot coals and eaten out of hand.[2]

But why Joshua tree—the current name for it on the desert? The Mormon pioneers in Utah are universally credited with having originated the term, and there is a tradition, which has been communicated to me by

[1] Charles H. Shinn: *American Agriculturist*, Dec., 1891.
[2] *The American Anthropologist*, Oct., 1893.

CHAPARRAL-COVERED slopes in the Sierra Madre, California

YERBA BUENA (*Micromeria Chamissonis*)

This little plant until a century ago covered the hills where San Francisco now stands, and gave its name *Yerba Buena* to the Mexican village out of which San Francisco grew.

Photo by L. L. Haskin

BITTER-ROOT (*Lewisia rediviva*)

one who had it from a Mormon apostle, to the effect that the wide-spreading branches of the tree seen against the night reminded the pioneers of the time when Joshua, the Hebrew leader, had his arms held up in the course of a certain battle in order to win the fight. I would have more confidence in this explanation if the Bible confirmed the episode. As a matter of fact, (Exodus xvii: 8–13) I find it was Moses, not Joshua, whose arms were so upheld, while Joshua was in the thick of the fray! The curious may compare this with a passage in the Book of Joshua, Chapter viii, in which Joshua is described as keeping his spear outstretched while the destruction of an enemy city was effected by his army.

Perhaps therein lies the explanation. Or perhaps the truth lies in another tradition, which is this: In 1857 the Mormon "State in Deseret" was in revolt against the United States government, and by way of consolidating power outlying colonies of the Saints were called in to Salt Lake. Among these was the settlement at San Bernardino. This was made up largely of converts who had reached California by sea via San Pedro, and presumably had never seen the Canaan of their people in Utah. Traveling Utahward through the Cajon Pass and out upon the desert, they entered the strange forest of arboreal yuccas of which a portion still remains. The distended branches, twisting and pointing ever onward, suggested to those latter-day Children of Israel a Joshua pointing the way and leading them forward to their Land of Promise—an idea with which their Book of Mormon had familiarized them. So in popular speech Joshua's name became attached to the trees. Thus, at least, the tradition goes.

Somewhat similar in look to a reduced Joshua tree, but with trunk either simple or short of branch, is the so-called Spanish bayonet, *Yucca baccata*, abundant on arid plains of the Mohave eastward to New Mexico, and the Spanish dagger, *Y. mohavensis*, scarcely distinguishable from the last but more distinctly a Californian in its range. Both these species are remarkable for their saponaceous roots, which from time immemorial the Indians have used for soap. The root (very difficult to dig, by the way) should be shorn of its bark and then crushed in water until suds are liberally produced. Few wonders of our southwest are more surprising to the tenderfoot than his first experience with this vegetable soap, which is as cleansing as any bought in the shops. The practical aborigines, however, did not leave off there in their use of these yuccas; from the soaked leaves they pounded out a coarse fiber for the manufacture of cordage, mats and so on; finally they boiled and ate the flowers, unless they had patience to wait for the fruit to form, when they ate that.

That same Dr. Bigelow of the Whipple expedition would seem to have been the discoverer also of our beautiful *Yucca Whipplei*, whose magnificent panicle of creamy white blossoms, rising a dozen feet into the air, illumine the dark chaparral slopes of the southern California mountains in latest spring and early summer. As the party came off the desert into the greenery of the Cajon Pass and the San Bernardino Valley, this yucca was seen, but as the month was March only seed pods clinging to dry stalks were found, insufficient for identification. About the same time near San Pasqual, in San Diego County, better specimens were gathered by Arthur Schott, one of the engineers attached to the Mexican Boundary Survey after the close of the Mexican War. Upon the strength of these, Dr. John Torrey, to whom fell the task of determining and describing much of the Western botanical collections of that time, was convinced that the plant was new and gave it the name *Yucca Whipplei* in honor of the leader of the expedition that had first brought the species to light.

Spanish Californians called it, and in some parts of the state still do, *quiote*, a term that has traveled far, for in the form *quiotl* it was used by the ancient Aztecs to denote the flowering shoot of the maguey plant. Of recent years one has grown used to hearing it called, particularly when in bloom, candle of the Lord, which very neatly meets both the poetic and graphic requirements of the case. I have been interested to trace the history of this expression, but so far without finality. It suggests a Spanish fancy, and one is tempted to turn it back into that tongue, as *Vela del Señor* or *Lámpara de Dios*, but the learned Hispanics to whom I have propounded the theory give me no comfort. Looking the other day through a number of the old *Californian Magazine* (March, 1882) I came on an article by Jeanne C. Carr, John Muir's friend and "spiritual mother," and in it she casually referred to the plant as "Our Lord's Candlestick," as though everybody knew it so. Further, I have found a suggestive sidelight in a list of Navajo plant names published forty-odd years ago by the scholarly Dr. Washington Matthews. Among them is included as the native name for a yucca of the Navajo country the word *yaybi-tsa-si*, which means literally "yucca of the gods."[1] Here I must leave

[1] *American Naturalist Extra*, Sept., 1886.

the problem to some other tracker of forgotten origins.

To the southern California Indians the splendid spires of succulent blossoms—as many as 6,000, they say, have been counted on one stalk—were but so many vegetables to be harvested, stewed and eaten, which was also frequently the fate of the tender young flower stalks. One can hardly wonder at that, for they look uncommonly like mammoth asparagus shoots. The plant is several years old before it is ready to flower, but the flower stalk once started grows with great rapidity, a foot or more a day having been recorded. The Spanish Californians were also fond of cooked yucca stalks. Their method of preparing them has been described to me as follows:

"You cut the nicest stalks of *quiote* you can find, but be sure they are young, fresh and tender, not old and dry and hard, like me," said my informant, an *anciana* of comfortable figure, with a humorous twinkle in her eye. "Then you dig a hole and put in plenty dry wood and set fire to it; and when the fire has burnt down to hot ashes, you wait a while till the embers get a little cool, just a little; then you put in pieces of *quiote* stalk cut the right length to fit the hole. Then you go away and let it cook till cold. That makes *quiote tatemada*, what you called barbecued. Some people put the pieces in the big outdoor oven, you know that kind? and let them roast, like potatoes; but I don't know about that way; maybe as good as my way; *quien sabe?*"

Then there is the familiar story of the strange alliance between the yuccas and the pronuba moth. When the plant is in bloom this little creature wings its way by night to a flower, gathers her fill of pollen, neatly rolls it into a pellet and carries it to a flower on an adjoining plant. The seed vessel of this she then punctures, deposits in it a setting of eggs, and clambering up the pistil of the flower pushes her wad of pollen well down into the stigmatic tube to insure fertilization of the seeds. Then, *vale* and exit. Weeks pass, and the second act of the little drama finds the infant grubs nosing about and hungrily consuming the plump seeds, and so the curtain rings down upon a happy climax. There is a moral to the business, too; for not all the seeds in a pod are eaten; the rest are left to start the coming generation of yuccas—an object lesson in conservation.

CHAPTER VI

Of Sundry Twiners and Climbers; the Chilicote
Game; and Who Dr. Kellogg Was.

S<small>CENE</small>:   *A roadside, with a chilicote vine clambering*
over bushes. Two little boys facing each
other.

F<small>IRST</small> B<small>OY</small>   (extending his closed fists): *¡Garambullo!*
S<small>ECOND</small> B<small>OY</small>: *¡Abre el puño!* (Open your fist!)
F<small>IRST</small> B<small>OY</small>:   *¿Por cuanto?* (How many?)
S<small>ECOND</small> B<small>OY</small>: *Por seis.* (Six—or four or three, as may
be.)

Now the first boy opens his hands, disclosing a number of smooth fat seeds, and the guesser has won or lost according as his guess is right or wrong.

So would two Spanish-Californian children in old times play with the seeds of Echinocystis, the big root vine, wild cucumber, old-man-in-the-ground, or, as the Spanish-speaking people say, *chilicote*. Sometimes the game was varied by putting the question "*¿Pares ó nones?*" (Odd or even?), and was similarly won or lost according to the answer given. So little does it take to entertain unspoiled childhood.

A remarkable vine is the big root, of which three or four species, all much alike, are indigenous to California, denizens of hillsides, thickets or brushy stream sides. From the monstrous, deep-seated root of an old plant,

54

which may be as big as a man's body (or as a flour barrel, to use the expression of a pioneer botanist) and weigh fifty pounds or more, numerous succulent little stems, like hop-vine sprouts, put up in late winter or early spring and poke inquisitively about in quest of a bush or tree to fasten themselves upon. Finding a support they rise rapidly to a height, it may be, of twenty or thirty feet. Sprays of smallish white starry flowers are soon succeeded by fat green burs of seed pods, softly prickly, that swing by their tails amid the leaves and form the vine's most noticeable feature above ground. When mature the bur cracks open at the lower end, and curling back its parted lips, spills out its crop of plump seeds, delicately brown or olive green. These are the seeds with which Spanish children played. In their tender stage the pods tempted American schoolboys of the rough-house sort to use them as a substitute for snowballs, for they had a satisfying way of bursting when a hit was made and bespattering the luckless victim with the slimy seeds and soapy pulp.

Then, there were more serious uses. Sometimes the seeds were roasted and an oil expressed which was rubbed on bald heads in faith that the hair would thereby be coaxed into being; and Indian medicine men, according to Chesnut, sometimes took advantage of the poisonous quality of the bitter seeds to make a potion of them to administer to old people hopelessly sick and decrepit, in order to hasten their end.

Bitterness, intense bitterness, also characterizes the "copious watery juice" of the root, and caused Dr. Albert Kellogg, who published the first description of the vine, to name it *Marah*, the significance of which, said he, "would be better understood by perusing

Exodus xv: 22–26"—"And when they came to Marah,
they could not drink of the waters of Marah, for they
were bitter: therefore the name of it was called Marah"
(i.e., bitterness). This name, however, is now obsolete.
The bitterness inspired some manufacturer of alcoholic
tonics, at one time, to use the extract of the root to
flavor his product, and in "Stoughton's Bitters," they
say, big root played a rôle in the Winning of the West.
It was also one of the plants formerly used by the Indians to stupefy fish, pieces of the root being crushed
and cast into streams, as described in another chapter.

Of the same family with the big root—that of the
gourds and melons—is that common California vine,
the mock orange, *Cucurbita foetidissima;* but while
big root is all for climbing, the mock orange creeps—
in fact, has crept its way as far East as Nebraska and
Texas, and southward well into Mexico, for it is by no
means confined to California. Its prostrate stems, sometimes ten or fifteen feet long and clothed with rough,
hairy leaves that stand alertly upright as a rabbit's, are
common on sandy flats and roadsides, particularly in
the South. The ample yellow blossoms are a copy of the
pumpkin's, and the round yellow fruits that strew the
ground in early winter after the vine is withered in
death have fooled many a tenderfoot, looking from a
car window, into thinking them refuse oranges. So well
do they deserve the popular name mock orange.

To Spanish-speaking folk the plant is *chilicoyote* or
calabacilla (that is, little calabash), immigrant names
from Mexico, where it has long had a reputation as a
soap substitute. You may like to break one of the
"oranges," mash up the fibrous pulp in water and wash
your hands in the cleansing suds. The carrot-shaped

root is equally saponaceous, but it is hard to get, for it penetrates deeply into the earth—as much as six feet, they say: an excellent plan to keep the plant alive through the most taxing drought. This is one of the plants brought to the knowledge of the scientific world by the great Humboldt and his botanical comrade, Aimé Bonpland, who collected it near Guanajuato "of the Mexicans," and were so impressed by the nauseous smell of the crushed foliage that they bestowed on it that specific name *foetidissima*—the very fetid.

You do not have to be much of a botanist to recognize the clematis, if you happen upon it in midyear when the vine is setting seeds. Then the tousled seed clusters, each seed with its long curling plume of a tail, are like a myriad silvery-haired, miniature Skye terriers, tumbling about over shrubs and clambering into trees. Three species are indigenous to California, two of them common throughout the state, in cañons, on hillsides, and amid the chaparral. One is *Clematis ligusticifolia* (that is, with leaves like *Ligusticum*, a plant of the parsley family). It is distinguished by numerous smallish white flowers in showy panicles—a lovely vine, "sown with stars," to use the Tennysonian phrase. The other is *C. lasiantha*, with larger, creamy flowers, each solitary on a long stalk, and silken of surface, which is what *lasiantha* implies. *C. ligusticifolia* has been called by Spanish Californians *yerba de chivato*, the "herb of the kid," because, it is said, sheep herders made an infusion of the leaves and administered it as a healing wash to wounded kids; which may be; but in Mexico, I read, another clematis is called *Barbas de chivato*, that is, "kid's whiskers," an obvious allusion to the hairy-tailed seeds. At any rate, the Spanish people in California have long had great faith in the curative value of such a lotion for cuts in animals. The undiluted juice of stem and herbage is acrid enough to blister a tender skin.

Indians also took an interest in clematis, and Dr. Kellogg has left on record a story to the effect that they used one species to revive horses exhausted by fatigue. It seems they would scrape a root-end and apply it to the animal's nostrils; shortly a trembling would ensue, and up he would scramble.[1] More easily accepted is Chesnut's statement that the peppery property of leaves and stems has led some of the California tribes to chew bits of the plant for curing sore throat and colds. In the days before government schools forced the fashion of short hair on the Hopis of Arizona, these Indians would make a tea of the hairy seed clusters of the clematis and rub it into the scalp to induce a luxuriant growth of hair, a great desideratum with them. You will recognize in this procedure an application of the ancient "doctrine of signatures," which not so very long ago white physicians gravely subscribed to—the theory that beneficent nature invests certain plants and other natural objects with significant shapes or characters that indicate their special use for the remedy of certain human ills. If a seed grows such fine long hair, what more natural than to assume that by consuming the seed you too will grow long hair?

God obviously intended man to love honeysuckles, for he has planted them around the whole world, north of the equator at least—some of them low bushes, others climbing vines that festoon themselves over shrubs and far up into trees. California has not been forgotten in the distribution of both sorts. Of the climb-

[1] *Hesperian Magazine*, Vol. ix: 587.

ing varieties found throughout the state, one, *Lonicera hispidula*, was formerly believed to be a good enough name for all, but present-day botanists consider there are differences sufficient to warrant separating from it two distinct species, *subspicata* and *interrupta*. Spanish Californians knew one or perhaps both of these species as *moronel*, and made a decoction from leaves, stem and root for purifying the blood and for renal troubles. This is not surprising, as several species of honeysuckle in America and Europe have found favor with herbalists as tonic.

Of the bush honeysuckles indigenous to California, two, I think, have an especial interest. One is *Lonicera coerulea*, the blue honeysuckle, a rather sturdy, dwarfish shrub a foot or two high, a lover of boreal heights and high latitudes of the northern hemisphere. It is to be counted a rarity in California, being found only in damp spots of the Sierra Nevada at elevations of 7,500 feet or so. If you see it only in flower, you will wonder why blue honeysuckle, for its blossoms (there are two on a stalk) are a pale yellow. Be patient and come again later, and the fruit will explain, for where the twin flowers were there is now one juicy black berry with a blue bloom. This berry is something of a botanical oddity, in that it is an amalgamation of the twin flowers' two seed vessels together with their enveloping bracts, the whole as effectually commingled as a scrambled egg.

The other bush honeysuckle referred to is *Lonicera conjugialis*, also a denizen of high mountains and more often met with. Its little flowers, twin-borne upon a long stem, are of so dusky a color as to make it small stretch of the truth to call them black—a character unusual enough in flowers to render this plant easily recognizable. It was discovered by an early California collector, A. J. Veatch, who found it apparently in western Nevada (where it still occurs, as well as in California) and brought specimens for determination to Dr. Albert Kellogg in San Francisco. The latter was attracted by the fact that the immature seed vessels, crowned by the two little flowers, were conjoined for about half their length, and saw in it a correspondence to the Swedenborgian doctrine of the heavenly marriage. So he named the species *Lonicera conjugialis*, adding for the commonalty a translation, bridal honeysuckle.[1]

This Dr. Kellogg, by the way, was one of the most honored of California's early botanists—the "blessed doctor" of John Muir's letters. Connecticut born, he arrived at San Francisco in the latter part of 1849, after rounding Cape Horn in a schooner with a party of gold seekers. He was then thirty-six years old, with a medical doctor's degree, weakish lungs and a depleted purse. His interest in the natural sciences, particularly botany, was paramount, and had been stimulated by a brief association with the great Audubon; so while others went gold digging, Kellogg went plant hunting, ravished by the riches of a novel and delightful flora. Even in that early San Francisco, of which we are apt to think as wholly money-mad, there were souls that loved flowers and all natural things, and one evening in April, 1853, seven of them, including Kellogg, met "to found by the dim light of candles, which they had brought in their pockets, the California Academy of Sciences."[2] Thereafter, until the time of his death, in

[1]*Proceedings California Academy of Sciences*, Vol. ii: 67.
[2]*Zoe*, Vol. iv: 1 (1893).

the spring of 1887, no name was more intimately associated with the botany of California than Kellogg's. He was the local botanical authority, and everybody with strange plants, curious to know what they were, carried them to Dr. Kellogg. If he did not know the plant, or could not trace it down in his meager botanical library, he would himself give it a name and print it. In this way he published descriptions of 215 species of Pacific coast plants that he considered new to science, besides naming a number more that did not get published and for which other botanists got the credit. As it turned out, many of Kellogg's plants were not as new as he thought, and only about sixty of his naming are current today. Yet that is excellent.

Personally, Kellogg was of a childlike, unworldly and lovable nature. When practising his profession in the East he is said never to have presented a bill, and one doubts if he changed his habit in the West. In an old magazine I find a pleasant pen portrait of him as seated at his drawing table in shirt sleeves and red-backed vest, happily at work on the beautiful and accurate drawings of plants he desired to illustrate; now and then relaxing by leaning back in his chair for a pull at his corncob pipe. He had a special interest in trees and shrubs. In drawing these he would first outline with exactness in pencil on transparent paper every particular, and then copy with ink on a sort suitable for reproduction.[1] Upwards of 400 of these drawings were left at his death.

Kellogg was a small man with reddish hair, and a devotee of Swedenborg. The latter's views influenced Kellogg more or less in describing his plants, creating allusions that have puzzled many a latter-day student,

[1]Edward L. Greene in *Pittonia*, 1: 147.

unfamiliar with the teachings of the Swedish seer. Dr. Torrey dedicated to Kellogg the genus *Kelloggia*, which the Wilkes U. S. Exploring Expedition turned up in 1841 on the Walla Walla River. It is a modest plant resembling a *Galium* or bedstraw, of the same family with the *Houstonia* or Quaker ladies of the Atlantic seaboard. It may be found in mountainous California woods and meadow borders in many parts of the Pacific coast, an odd little thing with the foliage of a Houstonia, the prickly seed vessels of a bedstraw, and tiny pink flowers like stars.

Among the plants often mentioned in the diary of Padre Crespi, who accompanied Portolá on his famous march up the California coast in 1769, was the *zarzamora*, or wild blackberry, whose lusty stems made thickets about the springs, fringing as with eyebrows these "eyes of water," as the Spanish phrase prettily has it. Half a century later Chamisso discovered it growing near San Francisco and placed it on the rolls of science as *Rubus vitifolius*, the grape-leaved blackberry. In April and May ravines, hillsides, river bottoms, throughout the length of California at low altitudes, are sprinkled with the snowy blossom of this rampant vine, which everybody knows. The berries are sweet and juicy, though varying greatly both in abundance and in character.

About the year 1860, a ranchman of Alameda County, Aughinbaugh by name, found growing on his place a sport of this common wild blackberry which surprised him by the peculiar deliciousness of its flavor. He transplanted the vine to his garden, where, under cultivation, it developed into a very desirable strain which in time became widely known as the Aughinbaugh blackberry.

It was from a natural crossing of this blackberry with a cultivated raspberry on the estate of Judge J. H. Logan at Santa Cruz, California, that in 1881 the famous loganberry was born. This love child of Aughinbaugh's namesake has made small fortunes for later cultivators and distributors, but poor Aughinbaugh himself is said to have got caught in the toils of an adverse fate and died in poverty.[1] The California blackberry vine, by the way, is notable not only for its edible fruit, but for the medicinal worth of the root. This is very astringent, as has long been known to both whites and Indians, who used to make—and doubtless to some extent still do—a decoction of the root bark for dysentery and the checking of diarrhea.

One April day of 1882 there set out from San Diego by wagon a little party of three botanists, C. G. Pringle, Dr. C. C. Parry and Marcus E. Jones, with a young man in his teens, for driver, who later became known as a botanical collector and whom many San Diegans still remember, C. R. Orcutt. Their purpose was a collecting jaunt into the Mexican territory of Baja California. That evening they camped a few miles below the international line in the valley of the Rio de las Palmas, Mr. Jones has told me, where they were ravished by the sight of a magnificent wild pea with remarkably large crimson blossoms in ample racemes, that none of the party had ever seen before. The long vines clambered over the bushes on the hillside, upon the dark background of which the flowers glowed brilliantly. The plant was obviously a Lathyrus, the genus to which the sweet pea of the gardens belongs, and the trio of botanists were unanimous in believing they had

[1]Charles Howard Shinn, in *Garden and Forest*, vii: 465.

found a new species, and a glorious one, making an auspicious beginning to their trip. But, alas, when the specimens were carried home and subjected to systematic study, it came out that six years before, the beautiful thing had been described by Dr. Kellogg from specimens brought to the California Academy of Sciences by J. M. Hutchings of Yosemite Valley fame, who had them "from southern California." Kellogg had named it *Lathyrus splendens*, and so it is known to this day.[1] Who the original collector of it was and just where it was found appear to be among the interesting mysteries of botanical history; though there is a tradition, as told me by Miss Fidella Woodcock of the Natural History Museum, San Diego, that it was first collected at Rosa del Castillo on the divide east of Ensenada, Lower California.

The plant is one of the most local of our wildings, being so far reported only from certain parts of Riverside and San Diego counties, California, and southward in the peninsula. It is particularly abundant in the neighborhood of Campo, close to the Mexican border, on which account it often goes by the name of the Campo pea. So spectacular is the sight of a bushy hillside all asparkle with the splendid pendent blossoms, sometimes as many as ten or twelve in a cluster, that a prosy name like Campo pea is by no means satisfying, and lovers of sentiment have chosen to call it Pride of California. Attempts have been made to introduce it into gardens, but outside its native state it is a touchy subject. It is too tender for the eastern outdoors, though it has been brought into flower there under glass; and seeds sent to Kew in 1894 by the late Prof.

[1] *Proceedings California Academy of Sciences*, Aug. 20, 1876.

Photo by J. Smeaton Chase

DESERT LILY (*Hesperocallis undulata*)

Photo by L. E. Martindale

FAIRY LANTERN (*Calochortus albus*)

Left: FIRECRACKER PLANT
(*Brodiaea Ida-maia*)

Right: HARVEST BRODIAEA
(*B. coronaria*)

FENNEL (*Foeniculum vulgare*)

Edward L. Greene of the Catholic University, Washington, D. C., bloomed three years later in a house devoted to Cape bulbs. In California gardens, where it may be grown, it is all too rarely seen. It is a perennial; and a famous planting of it on a wire fence, 300 feet long, on the Mission Creek Road, Santa Barbara, is a vision of flowery beauty every spring, and is visited by crowds. The color is very close to that of the ragged robin rose so often seen in California gardens.

Sometimes a person acquires a sort of exotic interest because he is some notable's relative. So with plants. There is a certain climbing wild milkweed, indigenous to arid sections of southern California and eastward to Arizona, which botanists once called *Sarcostemma heterophyllum*, but now more often *Philibertia heterophylla*. If your fate has ever led you into cheap boarding houses where the odor of stale onions lingers in the corners and passageways, the experience will help you to identify this milky-juiced vine, for that is just the kind of fragrance it exhales when bruised. But the really thrilling thing about it, to my mind, is its kinship to an Old World plant the very name of which carries the fancy back to time's dawn—*Sarcostemma brevistigma*, the Soma of Vedic chant and ritual, whose expressed juice, they say, was the basis of an intoxicating drink once offered in the sacrifices to the great god Indra You may remember Whittier's lines:

> "*From tent to tent*
> *The Soma's sacred madness went,*
> *A storm of drunken joy.*"

If Soma's California cousin, a sober, modest little vine to look at, holds any such frenzied possibilities, nobody seems to know it. It did, however, long ago attract the interest of the Luiseño Indians of San Diego County, who until quite recently were fond of eating it salad-fashion, raw with a pinch of salt.[1]

[1]Sparkman, *Culture of the Luiseño Indians.* University Press, Berkeley.

CHAPTER VII

Of Amole, *Which Is Both Soap and Hairbrush and Something More; of Ajo, Mission Bells and Three Mountain Lilies.*

O<small>NE</small> February morning during my salad days in California I was walking with my friend the Professor along a grassy arroyo bank when my curiosity was aroused by a succession of small potholes a few inches deep, freshly dug in the black earth.

"What animal," I asked, "has been burrowing here?"

"Probably *Homo sapiens*, variety *mexicanus*," he replied, "in quest of soap."

"*Amole*," he explained in reply to my incredulous look; "bulbs of a plant allied to Camassia, which the Spanish Californians and the Indians before them have used for generations in place of soap. There is an undug plant"—and he pointed with his stick to a clump of coarse grass-like leaves with broad blades and wavy margins lolling on the ground. "Should you dig it up you would have in your hand a bottle-shaped bunch of coarse brown fibers; strip them off and you find at the heart of them a white mucilaginous bulb. Crush this up in water, and you get a lather that is cleansing just as soap is, without costing you a penny—a boon to impecunious washer folk."

So do I introduce you to a relative of the Lily, *Chlorogalum pomeridianum*, found throughout the length of California in stony ground of valleys and foothills, and commonly known as soap-plant when not given its Mexican name *amole,* another of those Aztequisms with which California is sprinkled. It was among the very first California plants to become known to Europeans, and was introduced into England as long ago as 1819, "from Mexico," but that in those days would include California. Sir William Jackson Hooker tells of Kew Gardens receiving bulbs in 1855 from China, where thrifty Chinese laundrymen returning from California had, he states, introduced the plant for the sake of the bulbs for use as a soap substitute. The coarse fiber that envelops the bulb was formerly utilized by the aborigines for making rude brushes— hair and otherwise—after the soapiness of the bulb was all squeezed out. These were called *escovét* by the Spanish-speaking Indians, their way of saying *escobeta,* that is, little broom. As a garden subject, the use to which the English put it, it could have been interesting mainly as a floral curiosity. In midsummer the leaves wither away and the flower stalk shoots up, sometimes to a height of ten feet, though usually much less, bearing an airy panicle of small lily-like flowers, white with a purple midrib, the segments turned jauntily back like pigmy martagons. They open only in the late afternoon, which is what that formidable word *pomeridianum* means.

Not only soap and hairbrushes did this surprising plant furnish the aborigines. The tender leaf shoots, fresh from their earthy cradle, resemble young blades of corn, and were consumed as greens; and some tribes are even said to have eaten the bulbs, but only after the saponaceous juice was cooked out. This juice has a curious effect upon fish, stupefying them without affecting their edibility. Some aboriginal genius discovered this long ago and made the knowledge practical, thereby reducing fishing to a lazy man's job. A crude dam of branches would be built across a stream, a quantity of the crushed bulbs tossed in and well stirred about in the water. By and by the drowsy fishes would float belly up to the surface, to be leisurely brought to basket by the waiting redman. The first white comers into California were not always averse to fishing in that way, too, but this unsportsmanlike practice is nowadays illegal.

A similar property is inherent in some other California plants, which were formerly utilized in the same way. One is that common gray weed of stubble fields and fallow valley lands, Turkey-mullein or dove-weed, the botanists' *Eremocarpus setigerus*, called by the Spanish-speaking population *yerba del pescado*, that is, fish-weed. And then there is *Datisca glomerata*, or durango-root, a coarse, nettle-ish-looking plant of dry stream beds in the foothills. For years I was disinclined to have anything to do with it, thinking it indeed some species of nettle, until I found that its herbage was innocent of sting and no nettle at all. The intensely bitter root "makes fish drunk" in the same way as *amole*.

To return to our lilies. There occurs on both the Colorado and Mohave deserts a flower so like an Easter-lily as to delude the novice into thinking it is that, gone wild. However, it is not a true lily, though indeed of the family. Its name is *Hesperocallis undulata*, or in every-day parlance, desert-lily. *Hesperocallis* means western beauty, and Dr. Asa Gray, who devised the word to fit the case, never did a better bit of naming. After the winter rains the leaves appear in the form of a rosette

close to the ground—elongated, narrow, ruffle-edged
leaves, bluish green and bordered delicately by a line
of white. Desert children know them as heralds of the
lovely flowers and have been known to compete for the
future blossoms by drawing circles in the sand about
the leaves to preëmpt their claims. In early spring the
leafy rosette gives birth to a raceme of floral buds,
which break in the fullness of time into white funnel-
form lilies, six-parted, each fair segment with a bluish-
green band down the middle of the back. The small
white bulb from which they spring is deep seated, a foot
and a half below the surface, it may be; and if the
winter be one of scant rainfall, it takes a holiday from
flowering and bides a damper year. Given a normal
rainfall, however, there will be anywhere from a dozen
to twenty blooms, or even more, which expand two or
three at a time, opening upward on the stalk until the
tip is reached,[1] and parts of the desert become lily
gardens because of the abundance of this delightful
flower. Its range extends across the Colorado River into
western Arizona, where, among the Spanish-speaking
people, it is called *ajo*, a word meaning garlic, for the
onion-flavored little bulbs long ago found their way
into the Indians' cookery. The Ajo Mountains in southwestern Arizona owe their name to the prevalence there
of the Hesperocallis.

We are so used to flowers in gay colors that when one
presents itself in sober brown it is noteworthy. One that
so qualifies is *Fritillaria biflora*, the so-called mission-

---

[1]Francis M. Fultz, in his excellent book *Lily, Iris and Orchid of
Southern California*, reports as many as forty flowers on one
stem as not uncommon if the autumn or early winter rains have
been heavy.

bells, chocolate-lily or black-lily, which displays its dusky bells of bloom on grassy hills in early spring from San Luis Obispo County southward. It appears to have been discovered first by David Douglas, and the name *biflora* was based on specimens that evidently bore but two flowers. As a matter of fact, the number varies greatly; as few as one and as many as ten have been found. Fritillaria is a genus of wide distribution throughout the northern hemisphere, both in the Old World and the New, California having a baker's dozen out of a half hundred known species. Of all our Lily cousins it is perhaps the closest in relationship to the true lilies, with which old-time botanists often included them. All fritillarias, by the way, are not somber-flowered, though tones of brown and blackish purple predominate. One species is yellow, one is scarlet and another is a greenish white. In some the flowers are noticeably mottled or checkered. Of this sort is the scarlet fritillary, *F. recurva*, a striking species of northern California, discovered in 1848 by Hartweg. Learning of a party of Upper Sacramento Valley settlers going into the Sierra Nevada for lumber, he joined them for company. One noon, as they halted at the edge of a pine forest for the customary rest, during which his companions shot a deer, Hartweg went plant hunting and bagged several novelties, including this exquisite flower, the showiest of all the fritillaries. It is purplish scarlet without, and yellow or orange within, checked with scarlet which turns in age to crimson and purple. Usually the flower stalk bears but three or four blossoms, but Mrs. Elizabeth Parsons-Hawver, in her *Wild Flowers of California*, is authority for stating that thirty-five have been counted upon a single stem.

After all this about the Lily's California cousins—
and the half has not been told—shall nothing be said
of the state's true lilies? About two or three of them,
yes; for they have associations that I find interesting.
Very famous among them is *Lilium Washingtonianum*,
the Washington or Shasta lily, native to dry, sunny
woodlands and chaparral tangles of the Sierra Nevada
northward to Shasta and the Cascades of Oregon, its
white flowers that "look frankly forwards and upwards"
(to use Dr. Kellogg's words) breathing a fragrance as
of pinks. It was Kellogg who first described it to the
world. He tells us that the Argonauts of '49 were so
captured by its charm, that they called it the Lady
Washington lily, out of compliment to our country's
first First Lady. Approving the name, he Latinized
it, as you see. We have the testimony of John Muir that
the large bulb used to be eaten by Indians and bears,
which may account for its being rarely found nowadays
except where boulders and tangled roots give it sanc-
tuary. Lily fanciers the world over, where climatic conditions are not too severe, cherish it in their gardens.

Another Sierra lily is *Lilium Humboldtii*, which preserves the name of the renowned Alexander von Humboldt, although he never visited California and could
never have seen his regal namesake in nature. Why then
the name? It seems that a German plant collector, one
Roezl, visited California in 1869 and on September 14th
of that year, which happened to be the hundredth
anniversary of Humboldt's birth, he discovered this
new lily somewhere in the Sierra Nevada, and the sentiment of the coincidence inspired the name. Unlike the
Washington lily, which leaves the Sierras only to spread
northward, the Humboldt lily's impulse is southward,

reappearing in the Ventura, Sierra Madre and San Bernardino ranges, where its open racemes of orange-red bloom, purple dotted, are among the noblest sights of the cañons of the upper chaparral. The stout stem, four or five feet high, holds aloft a magnificent panicle of long-stalked drooping buds and open flowers to the number, at times, of fifty or even more fairly turning themselves inside out in the joy of blooming. Indeed, Mr. Theodore Payne informs me that in one case he counted seventy-four!

One lily more and my chapter is done. In 1876 Dr. C. C. Parry spent several months botanizing on the mountains and deserts of southern California, and in July visited the Ring Brothers' ranch at the head of Edgar Cañon, near the present resort of Oak Glen. The ranchers were raising potatoes and reclaiming for that and other agricultural purposes some of the *ciénagas* or damp spots on their land. In one of these *ciénagas* Parry was attracted by the colonies of a yellow lily of peculiarly delicious fragrance, which was new to him, and proved to be new to science. It was later dedicated to its discoverer as *Lilium Parryi*. In those early days it was abundant at several stations in the San Bernardino Mountains, the Sierra Madre and on Mount San Jacinto, but so outrageously have campers, motorists and commercial bulb collectors rifled its haunts that it now seems to be on the highroad to extermination, and the law has been invoked for its protection.

Meantime, this lemon-lily, as it is called in the language of the people, has been introduced into gardens both in this country and abroad, so that whatever the issue in the wild the world is not likely to lose it. That Dr. Parry whose name it bears has long since been

gathered to his fathers, but his memory is assured in
California not only in this lovely lily but in the names
of more than thirty other plants indigenous to the state,
some of them among the most charming of our wild
flowers. We have the testimony of many of his comrades
that he was one of the kindliest and most lovable of the
devotees to the "amiable science" whose annals he
adorns. It was he who named and first described *Pinus
Torreyana*, the peculiar pine to which Dr. Le Conte had
called his attention as growing on the coast bluffs near
Del Mar, where it still flourishes, annually attracting
hundreds of plant lovers who wish to see the little tree
on its native heath.

CHAPTER VIII

*Of Nuttall's Dogwood and Its Pigmy Cousin;
and Something of Nuttall Himself.*

A SPECTACULAR sight is the flowering of *Cornus
Nuttallii*. This noble dogwood of the Pacific coast might
be mistaken for the so-called flowering dogwood of the
Atlantic states, because of the large, showy petal-like
floral bracts that are a feature of both species; but a
critical inspection reveals differences, notably the perfect outline and larger size of the westerner's daintily
pointed bracts, while in the eastern species these are
in a way marred by a dark scallop bitten out of the
apex. The reason for this difference is interesting. The
flower buds in both cases are set during the summer,
remaining more or less stationary until spring. In the
case of the eastern species the incipient bracts form a
complete cap over the immature flower cluster with the
four tips pinched into a little peak, and when the imprisoned flowers begin to swell in the spring and the
cap splits and spreads, the tips remain rigid as though
the winter cold had benumbed them, and remain as
discolored scars on the expanded white bracts. In the
case of the Pacific species, however, the baby bracts
do not enclose the flower cluster but are borne beneath
it, where they snugly stay throughout the winter, and
once spring gives the signal to grow, develop unre-
strictedly and unmarred.

75

While Nuttall's dogwood is abundant along stream banks and in damp places in certain parts of the southern California mountains, it is preëminently a tree of the north. It is one of Yosemite's loveliest sights in May, but reaches its best development in the coniferous forests of northern California, Oregon, Washington and British Columbia. There it sometimes attains a height of forty or fifty feet, and, according to Sudworth, an age of perhaps a century and a half. All glorious as it is in the early year when buried under its white mantle of bloom, it is as striking in another way in autumn, when every branch, to use John Muir's figure, "becomes a crimson flame," and its clusters of scarlet berries make flush times for the birds. Naturally so conspicuous a tree could not have escaped the notice of Douglas, who records in his journal its occurrence in the Columbia River basin in 1825, and mentions the use of its hard tough wood by the Canadian *voyageurs* for "masts and spars for their canoes." He seems to have considered it, however, but a form of the eastern flowering dogwood, and made no effort to introduce it into England, where the eastern species had already been well known for a century or so.

Ten years later, the sharper eyed Thomas Nuttall, traveling with Wyeth's second overland expedition to Oregon, discovered the tree in the Columbia region, and found the band-tailed pigeons levying severe toll on its berries. Specimens of pigeons and tree were sent to Audubon, then working on his monumental *Birds of America*, and if you have access to the elephant folio of that work published in 1837, you will find in it a picture of two band-tailed pigeons resting on the branches of a tree, noted in the title of the plate as

"*Cornus Nuttallii.*" This is the first notice to the world of the existence of the species, but a year later Volume 4 of Audubon's *Ornithological Biographies* appeared, in which the author gives a detailed description of this "superb species of Dogwood, discovered by our learned friend Thomas Nuttall, Esq., when on his march towards the shores of the Pacific Ocean, and which I have graced with his name!" "Seeds of this new species of Cornus," he adds, "were sent by me to Lord Ravensworth and have germinated, so that this beautiful production of the rich valley of the Columbia River may now be seen in the vicinity of London, and in the grounds of the nobleman mentioned near Newcastle-upon-Tyne." Unfortunately for the horticultural hopes built upon it, this "noblest of the Cornels," as it has been called, does not take kindly to the English climate, nor, so far as I can learn, to the conditions of our eastern Atlantic states.

Also accompanying the Wyeth expedition with Nuttall was the latter's friend Dr. John K. Townsend, a Philadelphia ornithologist, who left a journal of the trip. (It was Townsend, by the way, who obtained the specimens of band-tailed pigeons from which Audubon made his picture of these birds.) In this journal he tells of a use for the bark of Nuttall's dogwood which is interesting. The scene is Townsend's camp on a plain near Fort Vancouver on the Columbia, and the time the middle of May, 1834. Near by are several lodges of the Cowlitz Indians, and in one are two children sick with intermittent fever. At the request of the parents, the doctor undertakes their cure. "My stock of quinine being exhausted," he writes, "I determined to substitute an extract of the bark of the Dogwood (*Cornus Nuttallii*), and taking one of the parents into the wood with his blanket, I soon chipped off a plentiful supply, returned, boiled it in his own kettle, and completed the preparation in his lodge, with most of the Indians standing by and staring at me to comprehend the process. This was exactly what I wished, and as I proceeded, I took some pains to explain the whole matter to them in order that they might at a future time be enabled to make use of a really valuable medicine which grows abundantly everywhere throughout the country. . . . I administered to each of the children about a scruple of the extract per day. The second day they escaped the paroxysm, and on the third were entirely well." The bark is bitter and tonic, qualities that distinguish most if not all of the western species of dogwood, of which there are several without the conspicuous, snowy circle of bracts that are the glory of Nuttall's namesake.

A miniature of Nuttall's dogwood, in respect of its white-bracted inflorescence, is the bunch-berry, *Cornus canadensis*, a charming little thing a few inches high. It spreads industriously by underground rootstocks, and snowily stars the floor of many a cool, damp woodland from the upper end of California northward to Alaska, inching its way thence across British America to our north Atlantic states. In the autumn, its bunches of vivid red berries give you the reason of its vernacular name. It is grown to some extent in English bog gardens. Peter Collinson, the English correspondent of John Bartram, had it in his famous garden at Mill Hill near London in the mid-eighteenth century. A note of Collinson's states: "Grows all about Halifax and Newfoundland [whence he may have had it], called Baked Apples and Pears"!

Apropos of Nuttall, he was one of the choice characters in the pioneer annals of western botany. At the time of his appearance on the Pacific coast, he was a tall, stoop-shouldered bachelor, rather stoutish and close to fifty years old, his bald head overflowing with knowledge of plants and birds gleaned at first hand from twenty years' contact with the living things in the wilderness regions of the eastern United States, into virtually every part of which he had penetrated. By birth an Englishman, the son of a Lancashire printer and educated while still a boy in the same trade, he had his interest in plant life awakened by rambles at odd times over his native hills. Early in 1807, at the age of twenty-one, he appeared, shy and solitary, in Philadelphia, where before long he made the acquaintance of that Benjamin Smith Barton, who, as we have heard, was Pursh's patron, and who encouraged Nuttall in prosecuting his study of the flora of the United States. Working at his printer's trade in winter, he devoted his midyears to long excursions alone in the fields and woods of the Atlantic seaboard, turning up many a plant never before heard of. In 1822 he was called to the chair of natural history at Harvard and the curatorship of its botanic gardens. There the year 1834 found him "vegetating like his plants," as he expressed it, when there came an opportunity to join Wyeth's second overland expedition to the Pacific coast. After six months of happy collecting on the way, he arrived at Fort Vancouver in September, 1834, and during the following year he was twice in California. On the occasion of his second visit he sailed from Monterey on the brig *Pilgrim*, immortalized in Dana's *Two Years Before the Mast*, working slowly southward and taking advan-

tage of the vessel's stops for hides to go ashore and
study the natural history, finally disembarking at San
Diego.

There, upon the beach one day, strolling barefooted,
and attired in a sailor's pea jacket, a wide straw hat,
trousers rolled to the knees and pockets bulging with
shells and plant specimens, Nuttall came face to face
with Dana, who had been his pupil at Harvard, and
who was now of the crew of the ship *Alert*, then loading
hides at San Diego for Boston. Of course Dana put him
in the book, for he was excellent "copy." "I should
hardly have been more surprised," writes Dana, "to
have seen the Old South steeple shoot up from the hide
house." To the sailors, seeing the queer man wandering
abstractedly about the shore and picking up what to
them were worthless odds and ends, he was naturally
enough considered more or less crazy, and they christened him among themselves "Old Curious." He left
California for home on the *Alert* May 8, 1836, and occurs
once again in Dana's pages. During the rounding of
Cape Horn, the temporary appearance of Staten Land
brought Nuttall out "like a butterfly" with the request
that he might be set ashore for a bit of botanizing on a
spot that probably no human being had ever set foot
on; "but the Captain," remarks Dana, "intimated that
he would see the island, specimens and all in—another
place, before he would get out a boat or delay the ship
one moment for him." A pleasant incident of his arrival
in Boston was the shipowners' refusal to let him pay
for his passage home. "We prefer not to take money,"
they remarked, "from one who has been traveling not
for his own amusement but for the benefit of mankind!"

And so back to the quiet of Philadelphia and the

Photo by L. L. Haskin

Dog-Tooth Violet (*Erythronium* sp.)

Avalanche Lilies, Mt. Rainier National Park (*Erythronium montanum*)

Photo by L. L. Haskin

YELLOW POND LILIES, Oregon (*Nymphæa polysepala*)

Academy of Natural Sciences to work up the results of his Pacific collection. These were published in 1840 in the *Transactions of the American Philosophical Society*, that venerable institution of learning of which Thomas Jefferson was for many years the president, finding in the tranquil pursuits of science, as he tells us, a supreme delight. Then one day the post brought Nuttall the unwelcome news that an uncle had died and bequeathed him a farm near Liverpool on condition that he would spend at least nine months of each year in England. A pent-up English farm, encumbered with annuities and income taxes, was no equivalent to Nuttall for the virgin fields of the New World, rich in scientific possibilities, and he would have declined the inheritance out of hand, but for the fact that the acceptance would enable him to give needed assistance to a number of nephews and nieces. The rest of his life—seventeen years—was accordingly spent as a plain English farmer, working and eating with his laborers, save for one visit to the United States (1847–48) cleverly accomplished by bunching the last three months of one year with the first three of the next, thereby securing a six months' vacation without violating the condition of his inheritance. He died as a botanist should, with flowers in his hand. A correspondent had sent him a box of plants from Asia, and in the exertion of opening it, something suddenly gave way within him, and he was gone.

Nuttall's memory is securely preserved in the names of a score of western plants. Next to his dogwood none is better known than the beautiful sego-lily, *Calochortus Nuttallii*, Utah's state flower, of which something has been told in a previous chapter.

CHAPTER IX

Of the Tree of Music, and How Wek-Wek Planted the World with It: How Hooker and Muir Found Linnæa; of Oregon's State Flower, and How It Went Abroad; and of Other Barberries.

ONE of the surprises to the newcomer in California is to find elderberries growing on trees. Unless he is a botanist, interested in scientific tweedledum and tweedledee, he will see little difference, except in size, between these arboreal elders of the Pacific coast and the familiar shrub of eastern fence rows. They bear the same ample compound leaves, the same pancake-like cymes of small white flowers, and similar clusters of palatable beady berries, though these last, in the California species, *Sambucus glauca* and *S. velutina*, are dusted with a whitish bloom, which in the eastern elderberry is not the case.

Among the California Indians the elder was "the tree of music," and flutes were made of the straight young stems, which lent themselves readily to that purpose because of the easily removed pith. You will see them in museums—a foot or more in length, open all the way through and blown from the top end. According to Mr. John P. Harrington of the Smithsonian Institution, whose knowledge of Indian customs, present and past, is encyclopedic, the elder stick was cut green in the early spring, and let lie for a week with the leaves

82

on so that these might "draw the sap out." This prevented cracking. The wall of the stick was scraped very thin where the stop-holes were to be bored, and a red-hot twig was then pressed against the spot. Only four stops were the rule, placed at random so that each flute had a different scale. Some players are said to have known as many as thirty tunes, some of them peculiarly flute melodies and never sung.[1] Moreover, as Indian music is strong in percussion, this tree of music was naturally considered the best source for the clapper stick needed at every dance. For this a piece of the cylindrical stem was split longitudinally in two, fastened together at one end, the free ends then being struck together against the leg or in the palm of the hand.[2]

Dr. C. Hart Merriam, in his delightful volume entitled *The Dawn of the World,* has recorded a pretty legend of one of the Sacramento Valley tribes, which explains how the elder has become so widespread on this coast, for it is found wild from British Columbia to Mexico. In the beginning, it seems, there was but one elder tree in all the world, and it was rooted in a den of rattlesnakes on a hill far away to the east, where the sun rises. As the branches swayed in the wind they made a sweet sound; both day and night they sang together. Now Wek-Wek, the Falcon, grandson of Coyote-man who made the world, heard the music and earnestly desired the tree. It was attended by two women chiefs of the Star People, to wit, the Morning Star and the Pleiades, who told Wek-Wek that the music kept them awake all day and all night, so they could work all the time and never grow sleepy. Yielding to Wek-Wek's

[1]*El Palacio,* July 1, 1926.
[2]Chesnut: *Plants Used by the Indians of Mendocino County.*

importunities, these wide-awake ladies gave him permission to take some of the elderberry music; so with his digging stick he broke off a piece of the tree, and from this planted cuttings throughout the land, in order that everybody should have music;[1] and so in some parts of the country there are found trees, the old Indians say, which of a night give off musical melodies sweet to hear—or, at least, so it used to be.

It transpired that in spreading the elder everywhere, Wek-Wek wrought better than he knew; for besides music, the tree proved to be a dispenser of other blessings—food in the berries, and medicine in the flowers and leaves. A decoction of the latter was famous for colds and fevers, and also by way of a lotion for divers "jointaches and other cold griefs," as old Parkinson would say—uses to which the Spanish Californians, who call it *sauco*, put it. Moreover, the elder is a tree of fire, for of its wood some Indian tribes made their twirling sticks for producing flame by friction. How did the fire get there? There is a legend, recorded by Dr. Merriam, that before men knew fire the Humming Bird stole an ember from the Divine Ones, and holding it tight beneath his chin (so tight that it has left a red spot there to this day, as anyone may see) hid it in a California buckeye—that beautiful little tree that is a marvel of snowy bloom every spring on dry hillsides from the Tehachapis to the Siskiyous. If this be true, it would seem as though the canny bird hid a spark in an elder tree, too.

A dainty member of the same family with the elder,

[1]Condensed by permission of the publishers, the Arthur H. Clark Company, from *The Dawn of the World*.

that is, the honeysuckle tribe, is that famous little trailing evergreen *Linnaea borealis*, the twinberry, lover of cool woods and mountain bogs of both hemispheres. In the course of Papa Linnæus's historic Lapland tour in the spring and summer of 1732 (though he was no papa then, but a brisk young bachelor of twenty-five in leather breeches, round wig and green leather cap) he seems to have first fallen in love with this delightful plant. Its pink bells in pairs nodding at the tip of tall threadlike stalks often greeted him in the dark coniferous woods of the North. In those days it was thought to be a campanula, but Linnæus believed it was different, and later on described it as Linnaea, a name that perpetuates his own, and which, by the way, he first had his friend Gronovius propose for it and so avoided, in the letter, at least, the bad taste of himself handing himself the honor.

In California Linnaea is rather a rarity, and has so far been found only in the northern part of the state. Its discovery was made under interesting circumstances. In September, 1877, Dr. Asa Gray, together with the eminent English botanist Sir Joseph Hooker, was in California, when they met John Muir, in whose company they camped on the flanks of Mount Shasta. As the party were gathered one night before their camp fire, Dr. Gray suddenly asked during a pause in the conversation, "Muir, why have you not found Linnaea in California? It must be here or hereabouts on the northern boundary of the Sierra." The next morning, while Hooker and Muir were crossing a small stream in the course of their day's excursion, their attention was caught by a green bank carpeted with what Hooker at once recognized as Linnaea—the first discovery of the plant in California. "It would seem," Muir afterwards wrote, "that Gray had felt its presence the night before on the mountain ten miles away."[1]

Another interesting berry-bearing plant of the Pacific coast, though of a distinctly different family from the foregoing, is *Berberis*, the barberry, also known as Mahonia. There are eight or nine species indigenous to California, three of which extend northward to British Columbia. They are evergreen shrubs with compound prickly leaves and racemes of small yellow flowers, which hold a pretty secret. When the blossom is fresh opened, the stamens lie back half hidden in the bowl of the concave petals, apparently dead to the world. Touch the base of one, however, with a pencil point, and up it flies, erupting yellow pollen at every pore. Now if, instead of your pencil, a bee, alighting on the flower, touches the stamen with its body, the irritable organ is similarly stirred to action, dusting the intruder with pollen, which is carried to fertilize another flower when the bee flies away.

Probably the most famous of our barberries is *Berberis aquifolium* (the holly-leaved), of which Lewis and Clark carried specimens back east from the Columbia River Valley. David Douglas, on his first visit to America in the autumn of 1823, found the plant in the course of visiting nurseries in New York and Philadelphia, and introduced it into England, where, according to W. J. Bean, in his *Trees and Shrubs Hardy in the British Isles*, it sprang at once into demand and for some time was very expensive, selling for as much as

[1]William Frederic Badè: *The Life and Letters of John Muir,* Vol. ii, 81–82.

ten pounds a plant. Later Douglas found it wild in Oregon, where on the banks of the Multnomah River (now the Willamette) he reported it growing to the height of ten feet. Nowadays a specimen of six feet is reckoned tall; half that is more usual. Evidently there were giants in those early times. Douglas sent seeds home, and by 1837 the price of plants was down to five shillings. Few evergreens from overseas are said to have proved so valuable in British grounds, where it is often planted as a ground cover beneath deciduous trees. Miss Gertrude Jekyll champions it in one of her happiest passages. "What a precious thing," she writes in *Wood and Garden*, "this fine old Berberis is! What should we do in winter without its vigorous masses of grand foliage in garden and shrubbery, to say nothing of its use indoors? Frequent as it is in gardens, it is seldom used as well or as thoughtfully as it deserves. . . . When one reflects that *Berberis aquifolium* is individually one of the handsomest of small shrubs, that it is at its very best in midwinter, that every leaf is a marvel of beautiful drawing and construction, and that its ruddy winter coloring is a joy to see, enhanced as it is by the glistening brightness of the leaf-surface: and further, when one remembers that in spring the whole picture changes— that the polished leaves are green again, and that the bushes are full of tufted masses of brightest yellow bloom, and fuller of bee music than any other plant then in flower; and that even then it has another season of beauty yet to come, when in the days of middle summer it is heavily loaded with the thick-clustered masses of berries covered with a brighter and bluer bloom than almost any other fruit can show—when one thinks of all this brought together in one plant, it seems but right that one should spare no pains to use it well."

In California this barberry is found wild in the mountains of the northern part of the state, whence it extends to British Columbia. It is frequently grown as an ornamental in Pacific coast gardens, but does not take so happily to cultivation on the Atlantic coast. Oregonians have a special sentiment for it and have created it their state flower. The handsome winter foliage in bronze and crimson plays a part in their Christmas decorations, and the acid, blue berries are often converted into jelly. Similar in general appearance and blueness of berry is the lower growing *Berberis nervosa*, frequent in coniferous woods, mostly near the sea. Both species are popularly known as Oregon grape, a name suggested by the bunched berries. Yet another species, *B. pinnata*, with similar bright, holly-like leaves densely clustered beneath masses of yellow flowers, occurs at thicket edges along the California coast from San Francisco to San Diego, and has acquired the vernacular name California barberry. It makes a good garden subject both in California and England, though too tender, I believe, for our northern Atlantic coast. In England it has been grown for more than a century—"a great plant for garden and covert," says William Robinson. It was one of the plants collected at Monterey by the Malaspina expedition, which touched on the California coast in 1791. Seeds were sown in the Royal Botanical Gardens at Madrid and produced flourishing plants, seeds from which in turn were sent to England. The wood of most, if not all, of these barberries is of a bright golden yellow, and has been utilized by some aboriginal tribes for the making of a yellow dye, while the bitter bark of the root has achieved a place in correct medical society, for its alterative, laxative and tonic properties useful in the treatment of various miseries of the flesh.

Rarest of all our barberries is *Berberis Nevinii*, discovered in the early 1880's near San Fernando, California, by Dr. J. C. Nevin, an industrious botanist of those days, in whose honor Dr. Gray named the species. It is a shrub six or eight feet high with extraordinary silvery green foliage and canary yellow flowers followed by red berries, which resemble currants and make a jelly quite the equal of those sprightly little fruits. So connoisseurs say. Only two stations, I believe, have so far been discovered for Nevin's barberry—one a sandy plain on the edge of the town of San Fernando; the other on the margin of the Arroyo Seco near Pasadena, discovered by Mr. F. W. Peirson; both close to growing communities. These are perilous situations for any wilding, and the plant would seem to be doomed to an early extinction in nature; though not the world.

About the year 1917, Mr. Theodore Payne, a plant lover and nurseryman of Los Angeles, realizing the ornamental value of this rarity, decided to introduce it into cultivation. It is what botanists call "a shy fruiter," and one season after another passed without seeds being secured. One spring the would-be gatherers arrived too late, and the birds had the crop; another year the weevils got it; and so on; but at last a season came with a crop abundant enough for all. From the seeds of that season a corner of the Payne nursery became alive with thrifty little plantlets, 5,000 of them, which throve and were distributed among gardeners up and down California and elsewhere. The species makes an excellent and interesting hedge, as well as a subject for specimen planting. Its story tells how a wild plant in peril of disappearing forever may be preserved to the world in the asylum of a garden without at the same time disturbing its last stand in nature.

CHAPTER X

How Frémont Gathered California Flowers and John Torrey Named Them; of Fremontia, Pussy-paws and Others; and How Carpenteria Was Lost and Found Again.

Most of us think of John C. Frémont, if we give him thought at all, as a political and military leader of a bygone era, with a penchant for western exploration, and let him go at that. Few are aware of that side of his nature which took joy in plant life, and how important were the contributions he made to the cause of botanical science in the course of his five expeditions into the unmapped West. From every one of these journeys he returned with sheaves of dried plant specimens upon which the stay-at-home botanists fell with avidity, finding in the worn and travel-stained bundles plant upon plant that no scientist had ever seen before. Of California plants alone there are a score or more that bear his name today and keep it continually in the mind and on the lips of the floral-minded; and these are but a fraction of the total he was the first to collect in the wilderness that lay in his day west of the Missouri.

Foremost of all the flowers that commemorate Frémont is that glorious shrub or small tree growing usually amid the chaparral of dry, rocky foothills and mountain slopes, *Fremontia californica*. It is most abundant in the central and southern parts of Califor-

91

nia, flowering in May or June—a most whole-hearted and enthusiastic bloomer, its large lemon-yellow flowers, backed with rusty red, lining every branch with almost solid color, and transforming the tree into the semblance of a tent of gold when seen from a distance. Mountain folk call the plant slippery elm, for they have found out that the inner bark is highly mucilaginous when wet, and can be used for poultices in the manner of the bark of the true slippery elm (*Ulmus fulva*), a totally different plant, which is not native to the Pacific slope. Another folk name is flannel-bush, probably from the grayish-white felt that clothes the under side of the leaves. Frémont discovered it, according to his label, at the "sources of the Sacramento River in the northern Sierra Nevada," and when Dr. John Torrey, to whom the "Pathfinder's" collections were submitted for identification, came upon the specimen, he had a special thrill in finding it to be not only a new genus, but a very remarkable one, closely akin to the curious Cheiranthodendron, or hand-tree, of Mexico. Now, the name Fremontia that he gave it was, so to speak, a second-hand one. He had given it not long before to a peculiar plant encountered by Frémont on alkaline flats of the desert, only to learn that this same plant unknown to him had already been given a name by another botanist. So Torrey had to take back the name Fremontia (for it would not do to have the same name for two different plants), and having it on hand he availed himself of the opportunity to bestow it upon this beautiful cousin of the hand-tree.[1]

[1]Many modern botanists do not consider it permissible to use a discarded name again, and these call the plant Fremontodendron, that is, Frémont's tree.

Collectors for European gardens and nurseries, following in the footsteps of Frémont, were not long in finding Fremontia, its introduction into Great Britain being credited to William Lobb, the famous Cornishman who collected for the Veitch nurseries of Chelsea in the 1850's. Since then its culture in Britain has spread among amateurs, and in spite of a climate so different from that of the parts of California where the shrub is native, it is said to succeed well in the protection of a wall. It has also found its way at last into California gardens, where, even when out of flower, its evergreen foliage, like diminished fig leaves, makes it an object of curiosity. A variety with larger, showier flowers was introduced a few years ago by Miss Kate O. Sessions, the eminent horticulturist of San Diego, who raised it from seed collected near Ensenada in Lower California. It is known as variety *mexicana*, and occurs as far north as Sonoma County.

Showy in a very different way and a curiosity of unflagging appeal is the California snow-plant, which Frémont brought from the "valley of the Sacramento; the precise locality not recorded, but probably on the Yuba River." The bright red, flesh-like stem, with fleshy, scale-like leaves, and fleshy flowers in a dense spike, so impressed Dr. Torrey with the idea of fleshiness that he made a Greek word to fit, and named the plant *Sarcodes* (meaning flesh-like) *sanguinea* (red as blood). It is a not uncommon denizen of coniferous forests in the higher mountains from the Siskiyous to Lower California, pushing its fiery head up through the leafy litter of the woodland floor in spring or early summer. One would infer from the popular name that it blooms in the snow, which is not true, except in the sense that a snowstorm out of season, coming after the development of the flowers, may temporarily surround it or even cover it with a snowy mantle. Some such event, it is not unreasonable to assume, is responsible for the name snow-plant. It is one of those strange members of the heath family of which half a dozen are indigenous to California, devoid of green foliage, inhabiting coniferous woods and uncannily flourishing on a diet of decaying leaves and rotting wood. Such plants may be red, brown, yellow or white, like the races of men, but never green.

In the case of *Sarcodes sanguinea* it has been learned that its roots do not come into contact with the soil at all, but are covered with a filamentous mat of microscopic fungus, which in return for board and lodging gathers nutriment from the earth for its host. Taking the place of root hairs "the fungus makes itself a sort of physiological middleman," to quote the happy figure of Prof. F. O. Bower of the University of Glasgow in his book *Plants and Man*. It is a case of coöperative life occurring frequently in nature and known as symbiosis. The snow-plant is one of our wildings that it is much less expensive to look at than to gather, a substantial fine being imposed for disturbing it in the national parks, as well as by county authorities in other parts of the state. Yet, after all, it is, I think, as John Muir said of it, "a singularly cold and unsympathetic plant. Everybody admires it as a wonderful curiosity, but nobody loves it as lilies, violets, roses, daisies are loved."

More responsive is the popular heart to a charming little mountain plant, also of Frémont's discovery, which forms rosettes of fat, paddle-like leaves clinging to earth or rock, and holding up to us endearing little fists of pink and white flowerlets mingled with specks of silvery chaff, which are the sepals. Some poetic lover christened it pussy-paws, and the name has stuck in the speech of the people, for pussy's paws they look like. Not so persistent has been the name which Dr. Torrey bestowed on it, *Spraguea umbellata,* for many present-day botanists reject it in favor of *Calyptridium umbellatum.* I, for one, am all for Spraguea, which was given out of regard for Isaac Sprague, who died in 1895. He was one of the most skillful of botanical draughtsmen, intimately associated for nearly half a century with the Golden Age of American botany. He did the drawings for numerous botanical works of Gray, Torrey and others, among them the picture of this pretty little namesake of his to accompany the description in Torrey's *Plantae Fremontiana.* Pussy-paws is a plant of the Portulaca family, and according to Dr. Joseph Grinnell, its tiny black seeds are much relished by the chipmunks, which harvest them with amazing skill, packing their cheek pouches with them and carrying them off to their granaries, presumably for winter consumption.[1]

Following Frémont, English collectors found it, and recognizing its garden possibilities introduced it into cultivation in Britain as early as 1858. I find it commended in mid-Victorian terms as a "very elegant dwarf flowering species of a novel character" for the rock garden, and I believe it still holds a respectable position abroad. Seeds sown in heat early in February, William Robinson tells us, then potted singly and planted out in May, will result in bloom by August or

[1]Joseph Grinnell and Tracy Irwin Storer: *Animal Life in the Yosemite,* pp. 193–194.

September. Such care does Europe consider due this humble beauty that our careless American feet go trampling on every summer.

Midyear campers in the yellow pine belt of the Sierra Nevada are not long in becoming acquainted with a gummy, scrubby little plant of the Rose family with small white flowers and finely cut, tansy-like foliage that mats the slopes of the mountains by the acre. If you are tempted to make a short cut across such a tangle, you will find your shoes and nether garments soon smeared with the resinous exudation of the foliage, and yourself enveloped in a bitter sort of aroma, which you may like or you may abhor. In either case, you will now be prepared to accept as entirely warranted the mountaineers' common name for the plant, mountain misery. Sheep, trailing through it, make quite a mess of their woolly selves, and the tinkle of their bells, tarred without and within, is stilled, to the discomfiture of the herders.

The specimens of the plant brought home by Frémont from both his second and third expeditions were in each case just enough to show it to be a new species but too incomplete for Torrey to make a definite description. Later, Hartweg, collecting for the London Horticultural Society, was more fortunate, and the English botanist George Bentham gave it the name by which science now knows it, *Chamaebatia foliolosa*, that is, leafy ground-bramble. A pleasant interchange of international courtesies attended this christening. Torrey, as the holder of Frémont's earlier collection, even though imperfect, might be considered entitled to name this fine new plant, and so Bentham, when possessed of Hartweg's complete specimen, offered Torrey that

Photo by L. L. Haskin

TURKEY-BEARD (*Xerophyllum tenax*) in flower and bud

CHILICOTE VINE and FRUIT

TURKEY-BEARD (*Xerophyllum tenax*) in flower and bud

honor; but "I thought," says Torrey, "the right belonged to him," and waived the privilege. Like most plants that bring on themselves the popular notice, it has several names in the vernacular.

Next to mountain misery probably ranks tarweed, obvious enough but undesirable because a number of other plants with gummy leaves and stems are also called that. Dr. Jepson records Jerusalem oak (evidently the work of homesick English folk who saw in it a resemblance to a wilding so called in their motherland), running oak, bear-mat and bear-clover. Touching the last, the late Mrs. Katherine Brandegee, whose pungent comments on plants brightened the botanical literature of a generation or two ago, explains drily: "Perhaps in accordance with our felicitous custom of giving names, because it bears not the least resemblance to clover and the bears will have nothing to do with it!"

Among all Frémont's collections there is only one, I think, that rivals Fremontia in beauty of flower, and that is the rare *Carpenteria californica*, a fine shrub with stems that slough off the bark in sheets resembling buckskin. The pure white flowers with yellow stamens clustered at the heart suggest a Philadelphus or a Japanese anemone. Carpenteria has an interesting history. The specimens brought by Frémont were all but flowerless; only a few withered petals clung to the seed vessels. Nevertheless, these were enough to show the plant's place in the vegetable kingdom and that it was new; and Torrey dedicated it to a botanist whose memory he wished to perpetuate, though in no way associated with California, "my excellent departed friend, the late Professor Carpenter of Louisiana." Then for well on to thirty years nothing more was heard of it; but in 1875 Dr. Gustav Eisen discovered in the foothills near Fresno a strange flowering shrub growing in considerable quantity amid the chaparral. It proved to be the long-lost Carpenteria. Seeds were collected which were distributed widely to horticulturists in various parts of the world. It was first flowered in England by Miss Gertrude Jekyll at Godalming in 1885; but it is about all that England can do to grow it outdoors, and only in the brighter, sunnier parts of that country does it succeed, and best of all against a wall. In such places it may be considered "one of the most splendid acquisitions from the California flora," to quote Mr. W. J. Bean in *Trees and Shrubs Hardy in the British Isles.*

Of late years, since the indigenous plants of California have been more and more drawn upon for the gardens of the state, Carpenteria has become better known as a garden shrub than a wild one. Indeed, very few botanists have ever seen it in nature. Dr. Jepson records but three known stations for it, all within a restricted area in the foothills of Fresno County, between the San Joaquin and Kings rivers. There it was, at last report, abundant in spots, whitening in June the slopes where it grows.[1] The foliage is intensely bitter; even sheep, they say, will have none of it—a fact that has probably suffered the plant to escape extermination by these "hoofed locusts." During the droughty midyear a more dejected-looking plant it is hard to imagine, its foliage wilted and drooping, its parched bark peeling, but with the first good rain of autumn the leaves stiffen and brighten, and the shrub is its cheery self again.

[1] W. L. Jepson: "The Long Lost Carpenteria," *Sierra Club Bulletin*, Vol. xi: 151.

Also among Frémont's botanical spoil were specimens of the western red-bud or Judas-tree, *Cercis occidentalis*, which he may have gathered in the western foothills of the Sierra Nevada, where as in many other parts of California the charming shrub stages a brilliant flower show of its own every spring. Clusters of magenta, pea-like blossoms break in naked loveliness from the bark of the old wood before the leaves appear. This shrub— sometimes a small tree—was for many years supposed to be indigenous only to California, but has more recently been found in southern Nevada and the Grand Cañon region of Arizona, thence to Texas. A very similar species is common on the Atlantic seaboard, and there are others in Europe and Asia. One widely distributed in the Old World, which has been grown in gardens for centuries, occurs in Palestine, and an ancient legend tells of its being the tree on which Judas hanged himself. The disgrace of this so shamed the poor plant that its descendants the world over have ever since blushed purple at blossoming time because of it! As though that were not enough, the seed pods, which abundantly clothe the limbs in late summer, blush purple too. All of which explains the otherwise inexplicable name Judas-tree. Among the California Indians the bark and young shoots of the red-bud are famous basket material, though baskets so made are not the most durable.

Frémont, I believe, was the first to record the marvelous spring blossoming of the Mohave Desert. In the course of his expedition that reached California in 1844, he entered that western tongue of the desert now called Antelope Valley, skirted the desert base of the Sierra Madre eastward to the Spanish Trail where it emerges from the Cajon Pass, then turning northward along the borders of the fickle river on which he bestowed its present name Mohave, he at last passed out of California into Nevada, whither we need not pursue him. The time was mid-April; the spring was at flood; the desert's gravelly wastes were a kaleidoscope of color. "Instead of green," writes Frémont in his journal, "the hills were purple and orange with unbroken beds [of flowers] into which each color was specially gathered" —pale straw, bright yellow, red orange and sheets of purple. Of them all he can name only the Eschscholtzia, whose masses of coppery flowers seen at a distance he at first mistook for variegated sandstone; but we who know the same region today can easily guess his vision of cream-cups, baerias, lupines and gilias in broad splashes of color visible for miles. Though hundreds of his gathered specimens were eventually lost in a Kansas flood almost within sight of home, the remnant was still rich in novelties. Among the many collected on the Mohave were the rare *Nicolletia occidentalis* (named for Frémont's first master in science, the astronomer J. N. Nicollet) and the delicious *Lepidium Fremontii*, Frémont's pepper-grass, a small evergreen bush whose bright white mounds of alert little flowers, delicately fragrant, remind one of sweet alyssum.

That Dr. Torrey who played so important a rôle in describing Frémont's collections—and by no means only his, but those of many other plant collectors during half a century of western exploration—occupied a place of preëminence in the lusty youth of American botany, shared only by Asa Gray, his co-laborer for many years. "My revered master," Gray called him, and upon Torrey's death in 1873 wrote a sympathetic memoir of him.[1] A teacher of chemistry, mainly in the Medical College of New York, and later holding a position in the United States Assay Office in the same city, Torrey had only off-hours to devote to botanical work, which was mostly concerned with the harvests of other men's hands. Nevertheless, he was enabled in connection with his government position to make two visits to the Far West, including California, and had the keen enjoyment of seeing and handling in their native haunts many of the plants that he had long before christened from herbarium specimens—plants in which for that reason he felt a genuine paternal interest. "Perhaps this interest culminated," wrote Dr. Gray, "when he stood on the flank of the lofty and beautiful snow-clad peak to which a grateful former pupil and ardent explorer[2] ten years before gave his name [Torrey's Peak] and gathered charming alpine plants he had himself named forty years before."

Torrey was a cheerful, kindly man, one of those old-fashioned scientists nurtured in religious faith, who rode unperturbed the storm that broke the Victorian calm when Darwin launched his revolutionary ideas. To quote again from Gray's memoir of his old friend, he "had entire confidence that the results of scientific inquiry

[1] *Scientific Papers of Asa Gray*, selected by Charles Sprague Sargent, Vol. ii: 359.
[2] Dr. C. C. Parry, who spent the summer of 1861 among the high peaks of the Rocky Mountains. In his search for plants in this rugged region, he fell into the way of associating some of the more prominent peaks with distant friends. To one such he applied the name of Torrey, to another Gray, and so on. "With such innocent scientific pleasantry," he confesses in one of his published papers, "I felt at liberty to amuse the solitary hours of my mountain excursions."

would never be inimical to the Christian religion, which he held with untroubled faith, and illustrated most naturally and unpretendingly in all his life and conversation." A year or two before his death he spent a winter in Florida seeking relief from a distressing cough. Returning in the spring, he was jokingly charged with having gone in quest of Ponce de Leon's Fountain of Youth. "No," he replied, "give me the Fountain of Old Age. The longer I live the more I enjoy life."

Among the many plants indigenous to California that today bear Torrey's name are three remarkable trees—*Torreya californica*, or California nutmeg (so called from some resemblance of the seed to a nutmeg, to which it is in no wise related), found here and there in the Sierra Nevada and the northern coast ranges; *Pinus Torreyana*, the Torrey pine, localized along the coast twenty miles or so north of San Diego and on Santa Rosa Island; and *Cercidium Torreyanum*, the well known Palo Verde, or green-bark acacia, of the southwestern deserts.

CHAPTER XI

Of David Douglas, and How He Carried California to European Gardens.

THE name of David Douglas is so continually cropping up in these pages—and will continue to do so, like King Charles' head in poor Mr. Dick's history—that it is as well that some particulars should be given of him and his way of life without further delay, for no other name is so closely identified with the introduction of Pacific coast flora and sylva into the estates and gardens of Europe a century ago as that of this indefatigable young Scot. He had the advantage of being at once an enthusiastic botanist and a practical gardener, with several years' experience on one of the great estates of the Scottish nobility.

During the first quarter of the nineteenth century the Royal Horticultural Society of London was active in searching the globe for novelties to beautify the gardens of the Old World, and stimulated by the increasing geographical knowledge of North America, they pitched upon Douglas as the man to develop for them the promising field of which Archibald Menzies, a generation earlier, had given a foretaste. Douglas, who was about twenty-five, of sturdy make-up, and eager for the task, was given accommodations on a brig of the Hudson's Bay Company's fleet, bound for the Pacific, and after an eight months' voyage around the Horn, arrived off the mouth of the Columbia River in the first days of April, 1824. From the deck he had his first sight of the magnificent virgin forests of that noble tree which was to be given his name and especially to commemorate him, the Douglas spruce, now so universally used in our architecture. His landing was in fog and rain, and the first plant he took in his eager hands was that western relative of the Atlantic coast wintergreen, the salal, or *Gaultheria shallon*, one of the plants discovered by Menzies. "So pleased was I," Douglas notes in his journal, "that I could scarcely see anything else," and among the first spoil that he sent home were seeds of this characteristic shrub of our northwestern coast.

For nearly three years Douglas threw himself with enthusiastic energy into the exploration of this new plant world. Making his headquarters with the Hudson's Bay Company's fur traders at Fort Vancouver, he traveled east and west in the watershed of the Columbia and south nearly to the California line, sometimes by canoe but generally on foot, a total, he tells us, of 7,032 miles, equal to twice across the continent. Up to this time the little that was known of the region's flora had been picked up near the coast by collectors in more or less of a hurry and often at unpropitious times of the year. Douglas, however, was not limited by time, season or distance, and his journals day by day record the finding of floral treasure, noted with an enthusiasm to make the plant-lover's mouth water. Of course, there were hardships aplenty, but what are they to a brawny young fellow engaged in a business he loves, but part of the game, to be borne with fortitude and lived down and to be laughed over afterward?

Oregon in those days was pure wilderness, the only

inhabitants Indians and a few fur traders; so, frequently for weeks on end he would not only see no "visage of his own coloring" (to use his own quaint phrase) but would be without a soul of any color to talk to, for his Indian guides, when he had any, knew no English. His journal for the day written up by the light of his Columbian candle—that is, a piece of resinous wood— and with nothing at hand to read, he would turn in for the night, often to suffer hours of torment from fleas or ants. Rats, too, were an annoyance at times, devouring precious collections of seeds and even invading his store of dried specimens. Once he records the theft of his razor and shaving brush by one of these conscienceless animals, which then returned for an inkstand, when Douglas dispatched him with a pistol shot.

The matter of sleep gave him great concern at first, for with the civilized habit of going to bed under a roof strong upon him, he felt there was something uncanny in lying down in his clothes under the stars, as his Indian companions did, and at first he must have at least a tent to shelter him from the skyey influences. By degrees, however, the dread of the bare night wore off, and he grew accustomed to rolling up in a blanket beneath a pine or sometimes an overturned canoe. Like John Muir, he was a devotee of tea on his travels— "the monarch of all food after fatiguing journeys," he calls it—but while Muir carried only that and a sack of bread on his outings, Douglas had a more catholic taste, and when his supply of civilized rations gave out he fared like his Indian guides on wild berries, arrowhead roots, camas bulbs, bitter-root and so on. A wonder that falls upon the reader of his Oregon journals is that he ever survived the wet of that state of the web-footed.

Rain, rain, rain, on almost every page, varied with storms of hail and thunder and lightning, causing continual loss of specimens and endless discomfort from eating sodden food and sleeping in water-soaked clothing.

And then the rivers and creeks to be crossed! Of course in those days there was not a bridge in Oregon, and he had to swim streams and at the same time keep his packages of plants dry as well as he could. Coming one noon, he tells us, to a stream thirty yards wide, which he had to cross in a hailstorm, the mercury standing at 40° Fahr., he swam across on his back, his arms lifted above him out of the water, one hand holding his precious pen and paper, the other his clothes and blanket. Two trips were necessary to transport all, and so benumbed with cold was he that he had to build a fire between trips to restore his circulation. That was on an empty stomach, too, for his breakfast of a little dried meat and a cup of water had been taken six hours before. To the Indians Douglas, interminably seeking and gathering plants, was an enigma, and Indian fashion they soon nicknamed him, calling him by a word in their tongue signifying "Man of Grass." On the whole, they were inclined to consider him a bad actor, because of his suspicious habits. For instance, he would sometimes make an effervescent draught for digestion's sake and drink it apparently boiling; he would capture the sun's invisible rays with a pocket lens and light his pipe with the heat of them; and to cap all there was a fashion he had of harnessing his nose with spectacles and doubling his sight! Surely a man of a dangerous spirit!

For all the drizzles and downpours of Oregon,

Douglas seems to have preferred them to the dryness and higher temperature of California where he later spent something over a year and a half, mostly in the region between San Francisco and Santa Barbara, collecting, in that time, it is said, seeds and specimens of about 650 species of plants. From letters to friends something may be gleaned of his impressions of the province, which he compared to Persia and Arabia in its heat and aridity, and thought that not more than three months of its year were fit to collect in. He landed at Monterey three days before Christmas, 1830. "Early as was my arrival on this coast," he writes to a friend in England, "spring has already commenced. The first plant I took in my hand was *Ribes speciosum* [our fuchsia-flowered gooseberry], remarkable for the length and crimson splendor of its stamens, a flower not surpassed in beauty by the finest fuchsia, and for the original discovery of which we are indebted to the good Mr. Menzies."

The wildings that have given our Pacific coast—and especially California—a world-wide reputation as a flowery land, are mostly annuals, the creatures of a season, their span of life from seedling to seed vessel covering but three or four months at most. The surprising discoveries of Douglas among this class of plants had a great effect in bringing annuals into fashion in European gardens, where, until his time, perennials were the main feature. His introductions revealed the varied beauty and peculiar horticultural usefulness of certain species of such Pacific coast plants as Gilia, Limnanthes, Phacelia, Nemophila, Clarkia, Godetia, Mimulus, Lupinus, Platystemon, Mentzelia and Eschscholtzia—a list that includes those familiar flowers of our road- and trail-sides which school children know as bird's-eye, meadow-foam, wild heliotrope, Chinese-houses, baby-blue-eyes, farewell-to-spring, monkey-flower, cream-cups, blazing-star and California poppy. As a result many of these commonplaces of our native flora, which we are carelessly ploughing up and obliter-ating every year, are cherished garden darlings abroad. In fact, so long have they been established there that they rank now as old-fashioned.

The garden's debt to Douglas, however, is by no means confined to annuals alone. His discoveries in-cluded also numerous Pacific coast perennials of notable horticultural worth. Preëminent among these is *Ribes sanguineum*, the red flowering currant, occurring with its less showy variety, *glutinosum*, from central Califor-nia northward to British Columbia. First noted by Menzies and later by Lewis and Clark, it was Douglas who introduced it into England, where its deep, rosy-red flowers splendidly enveloping the bush put it quickly into the very first rank of spring-blooming ornamental shrubs for the garden. The worth is all in the flowers, for the small black currants are hardly edible. Under cultivation several varieties have been developed, varying in color from an intense crimson to pinkish white. There is also a late-flowering double form. Another currant of Douglas's introduction, *Ribes tenuiflorum*, with golden yellow blooms, is both orna-mental in flower and fruit, the latter running a gamut of color from green through amber to cherry-red or even black, if the birds will spare them so long.

A good second to *Ribes sanguineum* is that *Ribes speciosum* mentioned a little way back. Its leaves are like the English hawthorn and the flowers like a slender fuchsia, and it luxuriates along the California coast from Santa Clara to San Diego. It is unmistakable because of its glowing crimson blossoms, with red protruding stamens nearly an inch long, making an excellent imitation of miniature fuchsia flowers, and thickly fringing the graceful, viciously armed branches. Few of our native shrubs are so fierily beautiful in the wild, or for so long, as this fuchsia-flowered gooseberry, beginning to flower soon after the first rains of the latter part of the year, and persisting until spring. It, too, was among Menzies's discoveries, and while Douglas included it in his collections, the honor of first introduction to the garden was anticipated by a certain "Mr. Collie," a naval surgeon, who is credited in the books with sending it from Monterey a couple of years before Douglas arrived in California. I suspect him to have been Alex Collie, surgeon of Captain Beechey's ship *Blossom*, which touched at California ports in 1827.

To the introduction of another most interesting if less spectacular shrub, Douglas holds undivided title— *Garrya elliptica*, which was considered perhaps the greatest curiosity of all his collections and of especial interest to botanists because it represented a new natural order. The name Douglas gave it was in honor of his valued friend, Nicholas Garry, deputy governor of the Hudson's Bay Company, for whose good offices Douglas had reason to be grateful. Supposed in Douglas's day to be only a shrub six or eight feet tall, it has within recent years been found to reach the proportions of a small tree when growing in rich moist loam. It is found from Monterey northward along the coast and ranges to southern Oregon, and is usually encountered on dry gravelly ridges, secretive amid the chaparral where the likeness of its evergreen foliage to a live-oak's may cause it to be overlooked by the novice. Closer inspection reveals the dark green leaves to have a distinct character of their own, silvery underneath and noticeably wavy margined. If you still doubt, bite one, and you will find it convincingly bitter; for bitterness is a diagnostic quality of foliage, bark and fruit.

The most interesting feature is furnished by the flowers, greenish in effect, which appear in late winter in slender clustered catkins of distinct sexes, swinging from the branch ends, charmingly festooning the bush. The male catkins are particularly attractive, six or seven inches long, each an interrupted string of little silver-gray bells, fringed with dangling stamens in pale yellow, whence one of the plant's popular names, silk-tassel bush. The female catkins are perhaps half as long, and are most noticeable in fruit, then resembling a short string of fuzzy white beads.

Garrya takes kindly to the climate of the south of England, where, I find, a height of sixteen feet and staminate catkins a foot long have been recorded. In the chaparral of southern California there occurs a species of Garrya with plane leaves—that is, not wavy of margin—*G. Veatchii*, a name commemorating Dr. Veatch, an old-time botanical explorer and friend of Dr. Kellogg, who described the plant. The bark of Garrya, by the way, has much the tonic quality of quinine, and was a common remedy among the pioneers for ague and intermittent fevers, whence another vernacular name, quinine-bush.

Noteworthy, too, among Douglas's introductions abroad are several genera of bulbous plants of the Lily tribe, for which the Pacific coast is remarkable, such as Brodiaea, Calochortus, Erythronium and Camassia, of which something has been said in another chapter— a list of rare beauty. Yet even more substantially than on his flowers and shrubs does Douglas's reputation rest on the magnificent coniferous trees which he brought to light, and which have become established ornaments on estates of the Old World—pines such as the sugar, the Monterey, the Coulter, and the digger; the white firs; and above all, the noble Douglas spruce, which Robinson has declared to be one of the best trees ever introduced into England for either ornament or timber.

Douglas's death in January, 1834, is one of the tragedies of botanical history. Two years after leaving California he was in the Hawaiian Islands. They had a bad custom there of trapping wild animals by digging deep pits in the open and covering the mouth lightly with brush. Into one of these hidden pitfalls Douglas fell and was horribly trampled to death by a savage bull, which was already there or fell in shortly afterward. His remains were discovered by someone attracted to the spot by seeing Douglas's pet dog guarding a bundle the collector had left on the ground just before he stepped to his death.

And now, after the lapse of a century, the influence of Douglas upon European gardens finds a reflection in our own; and our Pacific coast wild plants, like returned travelers who enjoy the prestige that comes from foreign sojourn and intercourse, are more and more finding at home the recognition so long ago awarded them abroad. The fact that so many of them are now having a sure place in our gardens may help us to regard with greater resignation their vanishing in nature before the inroads of the cultivator and the town builder.

CHAPTER XII

Of Pentstemons, Monkey-flowers and Chinese-houses; and Other Members of an Unusually Good-looking Family.

G$_{OD}$," says the Psalmist, "setteth the solitary in families." As with man, so with plants; no solitary flower but has its family; and the family of Scrophularia, or as others would say, the Figwort tribe, plentifully represented on the Pacific coast, is notable for the numbers of its handsome members. The genus Scrophularia that is responsible for the family title is mainly of southern Europe and was once held in repute as a remedy for scrofula, whence the name. In California there is one variable species, *Scrophularia californica*, a tall weedy-looking plant bearing a panicle of alert, little maroon flowers, which the bees haunt. California bee-plant, the country people call it—less beautiful, perhaps, than curious.

Well up on the family roster for beauty, if not at the very top, are the Pentstemons. The generous, tubular corollas in various shades of blue, purple, red, yellow or white, borne in graceful racemes or panicles, are among the showiest of our wild flowers, and in one species or another are encountered, giving color to every sort of environment from British America to Mexico—from sea level to alpine summits, on foothill slopes and cañon bottoms, on desert, waterside and plain. At least

(From water-color drawing by Chas. Broughton)

PRIDE OF CALIFORNIA OR CAMPO PEA

Photo by F. M. Fultz

Papaver Californicum   Amole Flowers (Chlor-
                              ogalum pomeridianum)

half a hundred species and varieties are indigenous in California, Oregon and on the northwest coast, the first noted, I believe, being the purple-flowered *Pentstemon Menziesii* discovered by Menzies at Nootka Sound. After him the thoroughgoing Douglas collected and sent home specimens of an additional twenty-odd. With the progress of the great exploring expeditions Pacificward, everybody got new Pentstemons—Nuttall, Frémont, James of the Long expedition, Sereno Watson of the King party, Thurber and Parry of the Mexican Boundary Survey, Rothrock of the Wheeler expedition, and so on. More recently industrious collectors like Marcus E. Jones, Tidestrom, Rydberg and Nelson have rounded out our knowledge of the group in the Great Basin and Rocky Mountain regions, where it is represented even more numerously than on our coast, until now well on to 200 species and varieties are recognized as indigenous to the western United States.

On the Atlantic coast the Pentstemons are almost as scarce as a ten-gallon hat on Broadway. Nevertheless, the East holds the honor of being the home of that species upon which the old Virginian botanist, Dr. John Mitchell, a correspondent of Linnæus, founded the genus nearly two centuries ago—*P. pubescens*. He gave it the name Pentstemon (which, as you may guess, means "five stamens") because of the presence of that number of stamens in the flower—an arresting peculiarity when it is realized that most members of the Scrophularia family have either two or four. This fifth stamen is notable in being without an anther, and is generally more or less bearded, from which fact the book-name beard-tongue has been accommodatingly provided for those sticklers for English that balk at

Greek. Nevertheless, Pentstemon has become as much
a colloquial word as chrysanthemum, and is easier to
pronounce, so it cannot be called pedantic to use it.

Because of their novelty in eastern eyes and the brilliant beauty of many species, few flowers are more
attractive to tourists in the western national parks
than the Pentstemons, and even the novice, when introduced to one, rather readily recognizes others, so
marked is the family resemblance in the flowers. Certain
species with slender funnels of scarlet or vermilion
bloom have acquired the popular name of scarlet bugler
or humming-bird's dinner horn, for obvious reasons.
One such, *P. Bridgesii*, makes fiery patches of color
in the Yosemite in summer, the invitation of its lovely
trumpets eagerly responded to by hovering hummers.
The bird thrusts its long beak through the clustered
polleny stamens, tapping the nectar pockets at the
base of one corolla after another, until the little beak
seems all of gold. So Dr. and Mrs. Hall picture it in their
book *A Yosemite Flora*. Thomas Bridges, "an old rambler and botanical collector," for which the species
was named, supplied the gardens of Great Britain for
many years with American seeds. W. H. Brewer in
Up and Down California speaks of meeting him in
1863 in the California mining regions, temporarily
weaned from botany and speculating in mineral claims,
like the rest.

The very similar *P. centranthifolius* is one of the best
beloved of California wild flowers, particularly abundant in the south, flourishing on the hillsides and even
on the sands of the desert. Its smooth bluish-green
leaves closely clasp the stems and resemble those of the
European Centranthus, or red valerian, the reason for

the clumsy specific name. This species was one of Douglas's discoveries, but I think it must have proved intractable under the alien conditions of English gardens, for I find no mention of it in British lists of today. In fact, most of the popular garden Pentstemons nowadays are a hybrid lot, progeny of the marriage of the scarlet Mexican *P. Hartwegii* with the fat-paunched purple and white *P. coboea*, which Nuttall discovered on the prairies of Arkansas a century ago and named from the resemblance of its flower to that of the familiar vine *Coboea scandens*. For California gardens, however, the beautiful Pacific coast species are naturally well fitted, and, as a rule, take to captivity good-naturedly enough if not unduly coddled.

Among the blue-flowered sort none is finer than the stately perennial *P. spectabilis*, which in a location that suits its humor will lift its great panicles of large blue-purple lilac-throated corollas to a height sometimes of six or seven feet. It loves the dry sunny slopes of the southern California foothills eastward to New Mexico. The joy of first discovery of this splendid flower seems to have been granted to William A. Wallace, an old-time collector of southern California, and correspondent of Dr. Gray's.

In our garden we get a certain satisfaction from the odd *Pentstemon antirrhinoides* (the snapdragon-like), a twiggy bush, which for six months in the mid-year, when other plants are busily blooming and fruiting, leads an idle, leafless and apparently lifeless existence. Then, with the first good rain of the winter, behold it breaking out brightly with an eruption of glossy little green leaves interspersed later with terra-cotta or russet flower buds, which gradually swell into plump yellow flowers, shaped like gaping reptile heads, the wide-open jaws lined with stamens. Its native haunts are along the western bases of the San Bernardino and San Jacinto ranges of southern California, and it is one of the plants that Coulter, on his pioneering expedition into the Colorado Desert in 1832, first brought to the knowledge of the world. Being yellow in a group notable for blues and purples and reds, it made something of a stir among the botanists when first announced.

Another notable western member of the Scrophularia family, especially on the Pacific coast, is *Mimulus*, the so-called monkey-flower. Perhaps mask-flower, the term sometimes applied to it, would be more accurate, for *mimulus* is a diminutive of *mimus*, Latin for a comic actor, whose grinning mask the plant's corolla, it was fancied, somewhat resembled. About half a hundred species are indigenous to the Pacific coast, if the shrubby forms are reckoned, though most botanists now prefer to count these latter in a distinct genus, Diplacus.

Many of the species are among the most endearing of our wild flowers, particularly some of the low-growing annuals that Dr. Gray classed as the subgenus Eunanus. Of these the dwarfish *Mimulus tricolor*, common on pool borders in the Sacramento Valley and northward, with relatively large rose-purple flowers spotted with crimson and gold, is one of the most charming, though *M. Douglasii*, with its maroon, slender-tubed, one-sided corolla, frequent on wet hills of central and northern California, is a close second.

Nearly every one of the early collectors added to our knowledge of Mimulus, and many of them, as Lewis, of the Lewis and Clark partnership, Langsdorff, Frémont, Bigelow, Kellogg, Palmer, Bolander, besides

Douglas, are commemorated in the names of beautiful species. Langsdorff's Mimulus is probably the most famous of the monkey-flowers, but has lost standing under that name. After being content to call it that for a great many years, and then *M. luteus* (an excellent name, by the way, descriptive of its large golden-yellow bloom), botanists now seem to have settled down to *M. guttatus*, that is the spotted, an allusion to the presence of the cinnamon-brown spots that commonly mark the corolla throat. It is an unusually variable species, occurring in one form or another along a large part of the Pacific coast from Chile to Alaska, and eastward to the Rocky Mountains. Menzies discovered it in California as well as at Nootka in the 1790's, and ten years later Dr. Langsdorff, naturalist with the Rezanoff Russian Pacific Exploring Expedition, collected it at Unalaska and sent seeds of it to Europe.

Its natural disposition to sport made it a darling of the plant breeders, and under cultivation both in America and abroad it has become the progenitor of a number of beautiful forms and hybrids, in tones of yellow, crimson and brown, single, double and hose-in-hose. In nature it loves the rich damp soil of stream borders, from sea level to a mile or more above it, a cheerful sight. The ample herbage and succulent, hollow stems were utilized by white settlers and the miners of '49 as a salad, under the name of wild lettuce.

Almost equally famous is *Mimulus moschatus*, the musk plant, cherished not so much for its yellow flowers, which are rather insignificant, as for the musky scent exhaled by its slimy, white-hairy leaves. Discovered by Douglas growing about springs in the Columbia River region and introduced in 1826 into England, it quickly achieved popular favor, and a plant of musk neatly trained upon a little trellis became quite the usual adornment of cottage windows in rural England, and later in eastern America. About the year 1900 it was noticeable that all the musk plants in cultivation suddenly became odorless, and in spite of fresh importations of seeds this cherished characteristic has not come back; so that *M. moschatus* in cultivation has become virtually a lost plant. To what extent this calamity has extended to the species in nature it would be interesting to learn. One wild variety without odor has long been known.

Of compelling beauty is the scarlet monkey-flower, *M. cardinalis*, another of Douglas's discoveries, the seeds of which he sent home from California in 1832—a wide-awake flower, alertly upright. Scarlet was a new color in garden Mimulus at that time, and the novelty of it made a real sensation when this plant first flowered in England. It still has a place in gardens there, as well as to some extent in those of home. It deserves to be more grown, for it takes kindly enough to domestication if humored with a damp situation—a reasonable demand, for the love of water is in its blood. Along the shadowy margins of woodland streams, its fiery tongues of bloom flash out against a background of dark green, and in favored situations are lifted as much as four feet above the earth.

The shrubby Mimulus, or sticky monkey-flower (*Diplacus glutinosus* or *aurantiacus*), has had a long career as a cultivated plant, having been introduced abroad nearly a century ago. Its abundant flowers in cream, buff, salmon—or sometimes brown—are suggestive of an azalea's, and one of my gardener friends, who was employed as a boy on an estate in Scotland, has told me of his former employer's pride in her potted Mimulus plants, which were tended year after year in the greenhouse as carefully as any other tender exotic. It, with the nearly allied *D. longiflorus,* is indigenous to California foothill slopes and cañon sides, and is found in flower throughout most of the spring and summer. It is an excellent garden subject for the Pacific coast, and if given water during the dry season, can be counted on, in the south at least, for reasonable exhibitions of bloom the whole year round. Quite recently an attempt has been made to popularize it in our Atlantic coast gardens under the name California sunbeam-flower. It is not hardy there north of Washington, I hear, but old plants dug from the garden in the autumn may be wintered in a cellar. Another striking Diplacus is *D. puniceus* (the purplish-red or pomegranate colored), a lover of dry hills in the southern end of California, notably in San Diego County, and is remarkable for its showy crimson and orange-scarlet flowers. It was discovered in 1836 in the neighborhood of San Diego by Thomas Nuttall, who supplied Robert Buist, a famous Philadelphia nurseryman, with propagating material, and the latter introduced the plant into England.

An interesting feature of all Mimulus flowers is furnished by the pistil. The summit is divided into two flat plates or lobes, constituting the stigma, that part of the pistil which catches and absorbs the pollen. When the corolla begins to part, like a curtain at the play, these lobes are discovered folded together, but soon they begin to open out, until, in full flower, they stand well expanded. Now, if touched with a bit of straw or a visiting insect's foot, they are irritated just as you or I would be, and shut up, but open again, cautiously, when the coast is clear, so to remain until the blossom fades. Of course, this little drama, which is interesting to the idle mind merely as a pleasing diversion, has been a source of some worriment to the scientific, who must have an explanation, and there have been many, though none, so far as I know, not disputable.

Choice relatives of the monkey-flowers are those lovely little annuals the Collinsias, represented on the Pacific coast by a score of species and varieties. Their name keeps alive that of Zaccheus Collins, of Philadelphia, whom Dr. Gray considered the most accurate botanist of his place and time. He was a contemporary and fellow townsman of Thomas Nuttall, who discovered the first recorded species, a native of eastern woodlands, and dedicated the genus to Collins. Collinsias, however, are characteristically western. Douglas, of course, did not fail to discover them and recognize their garden worth. *C. bicolor*, a foothill species, is perhaps the commonest and is found throughout much of California. It has been a favorite abroad for a century, and in a recent English catalogue I found it rather quaintly praised as possessing "the desirable quality of flourishing in town gardens"! The two-lipped blossoms, white or lilac above and violet or rose below, are arranged in horizontal, wheel-like, interrupted clusters, one above another on a common stem, suggesting the architecture of a pagoda, whence the happy vernacular term, Chinese-houses, for the flower.

Another interesting species of Collinsia was discovered by Theodor Hartweg one spring day of 1848, in the dry sandy bed of a tributary of the Yuba River in California. Though much less attractive than *C. bicolor*, the yellowish flowers mottled with purple were not without charm to him, and he returned later to procure seeds, with the result that he found his hands stained yellow by the glandular hairs that cover the pods. That gave him an idea for a name, and he called the species *Collinsia tinctoria*.

From Collinsia to Antirrhinum, the snapdragon, is so short a step that I am not surprised to read of Douglas's not being sure whether his first Collinsia was that or a snapdragon. There are several rather showy species of the latter indigenous to the Pacific coast, fine, robust plants, several feet high, with flowery spikes sometimes two feet long. They are easily recognized by their resemblance to the ordinary garden snapdragon. *Antirrhinum glandulosum*, the sticky snapdragon, a perennial of the California hills, particularly of the south, was thought by its discoverer, Douglas, to be of garden value and was introduced by him into England, but it did not get friends there. For California gardens, however, it is worth having, because of its charming rosy pink flowers with yellow palate, in slender spikes. Coulter's snapdragon (*A. Coulterianum*) in white, and Nuttall's (*A. Nuttallianum*) in blue, are also southerners, and belong to a class of snapdragons with half a mind to be vines, for they develop slender, twining branchlets from among the flowers. By these the plants climb, curling about the chaparral shrubs amid which they are often found.

But the prince of all the race on the Pacific coast is the rare *A. speciosum*, or Gambel's snapdragon, peculiar to Santa Catalina, San Clemente and Guadalupe islands. It is an evergreen shrub, sometimes as much as eight feet high, though more usually half that, and pro-

ducing in spring and early summer small terminal clusters of bright scarlet tubular flowers, most unsnap-
dragon-like. Indeed, not all botanists are content to
call it a snapdragon at all, but would consider it a
distinct genus, *Gambelia*, as Thomas Nuttall, the first
to name it, called it. The pretty flower was discovered
by William Gambel, a young Philadelphian of humble
circumstances, whose interest in the natural sciences
induced Nuttall (who, some say, was his uncle) to send
him on an overland trip to California to collect specimens of birds and plants. Starting from Philadelphia in
1842, he returned a year later with much spoil, and his
name is preserved in some notable subjects, as Gambel's
quail and Gambel's oak. It was during this trip that
he made collections on Santa Catalina Island, which
had never before been visited by a botanist, and where
he discovered, among other things, this rare and
anomalous snapdragon. In the spring of 1849 he set
out again across the continent, but he had barely
reached California after many hardships, when he fell
a victim to typhoid fever and died. His mortality rests
in an unknown hillside grave somewhere above the
waters of El Rio de las Plumas, as the Feather River
was called in those days.

And so we come to a very different appearing member
of our good-looking family—the Indian paint-brush,
Castilleia of the botanists, one of those peculiar flowers
that, like the jackdaw in the fable, make capital of
borrowed plumes. In other words, it clothes its rather
insignificant flowers with more or less gaudy bracts
which flaunt the colors that naturally belong to flowers.
These are usually red or scarlet, though sometimes
yellowish or even white, gathered into conspicuous

terminal spikes. It is an abundant plant of the Pacific slope, occurring in all sorts of situations, wet and dry, on hillside and plain and desert, by the seaside and on mountain tops, from Alaska to Mexico, and from the Pacific to the Rocky Mountains and the Great Plains. Indeed, it does not stop until the Atlantic is reached, though on that seaboard there is but one species commonly met, *Castilleia coccinea,* the well known painted cup.

As to the number of far western species, it is not for me to say; for Castilleia is one of those plants whose nomenclature has suffered many things of many botanists. Conservatives are content with a score or so of species for California and Oregon, which seems liberal enough. A few more are indigenous to Latin America, and, as a matter of fact, it was two of these (natives of Colombia) upon which the genus was founded by the Spanish botanist Dr. José Celestino Mutis. Mutis was quite a notable in his day, which was a century and a half ago. He went to New Granada—now denominated the republic of Colombia—as physician to the viceroy, and was so ravished by the novelty and beauty of the region's flora that it became a lotus land to him. He never returned to Spain, but died in 1809, in Santa Fé de Bogotá, where he had established a botanic garden. The name Castilleia was given by him out of compliment to his compatriot, one Castillejo, a botanist of Cadiz.

The plant is something of a sly-boots, for many of its species have a way of quietly picking the pockets of neighbor plants by striking root into their underground parts and sucking out ready-made nutriment. Such parasitism is the more reprehensible because it seems quite needless, since Castilleia has a proper root system of its own for acquiring nutriment in the orthodox way from the soil, and does, as a matter of fact, get most of its living that way.

Very similar in appearance to Castilleia, but irreproachable in its root habits, is its cousin Orthocarpus, the owl's clover. Who the poet was who first gave it this name, I have not learned, but anyone seeing a ground owl solemnly surveying a red-clover-like expanse of the lovely *Orthocarpus purpurescens* (a very common species) will, I think, approve the name. More intelligible is coyote-tail, which Mr. Chesnut heard Indian children call a kindred species of northern California. A characteristic feature of owl's clover that differentiates it from Indian paint-brush is the presence of one to three little puffed-up sacs on the lower lip of the corolla. "Charming," said I one day to the Professor, "but why?" "You'd be happier," he fenced, "if you took some things in nature unquestioningly, not imputing ulterior motives. Personally, I am content to accept Emerson's dictum that beauty is its own excuse for being, and let this owl's clover case go at that."

The superstitions of the Old World have had a great deal to do with vernacular plant names, some of which, brought by immigrants to this new land, have become part of our speech too. One of these is lousewort, an inexplicable word, unless you are familiar with the writings of some of the old herbalists, who explain it, as Gerarde does, to be a plant which "filled sheep and other cattle that feed in meadows where it groweth, full of lice." Less shocking to polite ears is the Latin equivalent, *Pedicularis*. The plant is of the Scrophularia sisterhood, and occurs in a number of species around the northern hemisphere, especially in the colder portions.

Probably the best known on the Pacific coast is *Pedicularis densiflora*, whose racemes of crimson flowers somewhat suggest a paint-brush. It is a denizen of open, wooded hills throughout western California. Indian children and yellow-hammers, Mr. Chesnut tells us, are fond of sucking the nectar from the flowers, and the Yuki Indian word for the flower and for the bird is the same, *wa-i-mok*. But of all the dozen species of Pedicularis on our western coast the quaint little *P. groenlandica* is, I think, the most appealing. You will find it in high mountain meadows of several of the national parks, as Yosemite, Mount Rainier and Glacier. The interest in it centers in the uncanny resemblance of its crimson flowers to tiny elephants' heads. The helmet-like upper lip of the corolla, which looks like an elephant's smooth forehead, is prolonged into a slender beak. This bends downward, then forward and upward, until it requires no imagination at all to see in the whole picture a miniature elephant tossing his trunk. A crowning touch is given by the drooping lobes of the corolla's lower lip, which resemble ears. So, elephant's-head the flower has come to be called, or sometimes little red elephant. It ranges from California northward to British Columbia and eastward through the Rocky Mountains to Labrador and Greenland (where it appears to have been first discovered, as the specific name indicates), doing its little act as faithfully before the scant audiences of the bleakest boreal regions as though all the world were gathered to see and applaud.

CHAPTER XIII

Of the Wild Peony; How Doña Matilde Made a Tea of It; the Story of the Larkspur's Debt to the Dolphin; and a Note about Buttercup Mush.

I MARVEL," remarked the Professor one January day as we sauntered along a foothill trail, "that the Spanish Californians ever died. They seem to have had a plant remedy always at hand for each bodily ailment, and many a one that was good for everything. Most of the doctoring in the old days was a woman's job; what they knew they learned in part from the Indians, and the rest of it came up from Mexico or from Spain. Now, there is the wild peony"—and he pointed to a lowly plant with coarsely divided leaves and curious half-globular crimson flowers of a leathery texture, glowing dully in the chaparral. "Our friend Doña Matilde tells me that when she was a girl nothing was esteemed more efficacious than *peonía* for dyspepsia and every sort of indigestion. In fact, even now all the old Spanish house-wives know it and prize it. The root is the part used. Doña Matilde says it must be boiled long and well, and when the brew is good and strong she takes a spoonful of *flor de ceniza* and stirs it in, then stands all aside to settle. Then you drink it down and all is well."

"And what is this *flor de ceniza?*" I asked.

"The flower of the wood-ash, the fine, fluffy efflores-cence of the ashes on the hearth, the airy, filmy bloom of them that a breath will dissipate; not the coarse part of the ashes. The Spanish like to inject a bit of poetry into their everyday speech."

This use of our wild peony, *Paeonia Brownii*, is, however, but an echo on our western shores of the stir once made in the Old World by the supposed medicinal worth of one of the sorts of garden peony that is native to parts of Europe and Asia and whose root was held in such high repute by the ancients for the cure of spasms, the falling sickness and nightmare (!) as to be accounted a gift of Paeon, god of healing and physician to the immortals. Hence their name Paeonia for it, which Linnæus found good enough to adopt and so perpetuate. Our Pacific coast species has the distinction of being the only peony native to the New World. Douglas found it on the Blue Mountains of Oregon, "flowering in perfection on the confines of perpetual snow," and was enraptured by it, but his hope of making a home for it in the gardens of Europe does not seem to have been realized, its modest charms being overshadowed by the showier products of the hybridists' art. Why he called the species *Brownii* Douglas did not say, but Dr. Arthur W. Hill of Kew informs me it was very probably in honor of Robert Brown, who wrote the botany for Captain Parry's *Voyage for the Discovery of a Northwest Passage in the Years 1819–20*.

When a flower that has habitually greeted you in a dress of blue or white appears one day all in scarlet, you are naturally treated to a sensation. This is what happened to the gardening world when William Lobb seventy-odd years ago found and introduced into England the brilliant *Delphinium cardinale*. Delphiniums blue and purple, pink and white, the world had known for centuries, but here was one in every particular as fine as any ever heard of, with the added excellence of a new and splendid color, for the flowers of this were a bright scarlet, borne in racemes sometimes a foot and a half long on stalks as tall as a man. In nature the scarlet larkspur is found only in southern California and down the peninsula, luxuriating in sandy soil or decomposed granite amid the scrub of dry mesas and hillsides and in warm cañon bottoms. It is a laggard in the floral procession of the year, waiting to put up its magnificent spires of bloom until after the dry season is well under way, even until August. Its earliest recorded discoverer was Dr. C. C. Parry, who found it in the mountains east of San Diego in 1850, several years before Lobb.

From Oregon southward in the mountains to central California are the haunts of *Delphinium nudicaule*, the red larkspur, a dwarfer, less spectacular flower than its cardinal relative, but strikingly lovely, none the less. Though discovered by Douglas and subsequent travelers, its introduction, at any rate abroad, was much later than the other's and has been permanent. Robinson, in *The English Flower Garden*, has a kind word for both species, though *nudicaule*, which has also proved hardy in gardens of our Atlantic states, would seem to be the more dependable. Chesnut has recorded of this species that the Calpella Indians of northern California have a name for it that means "sleep root," because, they say, the root has stupefying qualities that make it useful for dulling the wits of an opponent when gambling with him!

Of larkspurs in orthodox shades of blue or pink the Pacific coast has near a score of species and varieties,

CALIFORNIA BUCKEYE in bloom. In the Tehachapi Mountains

Photo by L. L. Haskin

OREGON'S STATE FLOWER (*Berberis aquifolium*)

occurring on seacoast, mesa and mountain, though rarely in such sociable gatherings as to color the landscape in any striking way, as certain other wild flowers do—the lupines, for instance. One exquisite species with sky-blue flowers, *Delphinium Parishii*, is peculiar to the Mohave and Colorado deserts, and commemorates the late S. B. Parish, who did so much to enlarge the world's knowledge with respect to the botanical wealth of those arid stretches.

"Not all the monuments of antiquity that have persisted to our day," I hear the Professor say, in one of his oracular moods, "are architectural. Some are verbal, ancient words imbedded in our language that have come down to us through the ages and somehow have escaped the demolition that befalls most words under constant wearing of lip and tongue. One of these ancient words is delphinium. Under the form *delphinion*, the old Greeks a couple of millenniums ago applied it to the larkspur, which in one species or another is indigenous throughout much of Europe and Asia. Its most noticeable feature, as everybody knows, is the long spur at the base of the blossom. It has a tale to unfold. It seems, according to an ancient myth, that a certain fisherman one day fell out of his boat and was like to perish, when he was picked up by a passing dolphin. The fish tossed him astride of its back and bore him to land. The kindly act so touched the fisherman's heart that some time later, when some of his comrades hatched a scheme to catch the dolphin, he managed to frustrate their plan and for his interference was drowned by them. Thereupon the dolphin carried the body to Father Neptune and had it transformed into a flower. Now, in the light of this story, if you will take a look at the flower bud of a delphinium, you must see that it bears enough resemblance to a dolphin's form to have suggested to some fanciful Greek the name dolphin-' flower, which is what *delphinion* or *delphinium* means. It is a far cry from the Greece of Dioscorides to the California of today, where the pretty flowers grace so many prospects, but I cherish the story as a mite of contributory evidence to the whole world's kinship."

To the modern mind, seeking names for the creation, the long-tailed flower seems not a dolphin but a spur— the spur of the lark to the English, Scandinavian and Teutonic folk; the spur of the horseman to Spaniards and Italians. My Spanish California neighbor, Doña Margarita, whose little garden is a riot of old-time flowers, has every spring a bed of blue larkspurs, which she calls *espuelas de caballero*—that is, horseman's spurs—and has always a pinch of the seed for a friend.

Apropos of peonies and larkspurs, it is not out of order to say a word about buttercups, for, dissimilar as they seem to the uninitiated, they are really, all three, of the same family, sisters under the skin. You must not, however, expect to find the common buttercups of eastern fields and meadows wild on our Pacific coast. Those are immigrant plants from Europe, and are content enough with the Atlantic seaboard to stay there. Nevertheless, the Pacific coast gets along quite well without them, for it has a score of indigenous species of its own, the commonest being *Ranunculus californicus*, which gilds with fleeting gold the grassy roadsides and valleys of California in late winter and early spring. The easterner has no difficulty in recognizing it as a buttercup, but at the same time is conscious of a difference from the familiar flower of his home fields.

If he counts the petals one reason is apparent; his eastern flower had but five, while this exuberant Californian has two or three times as many.

In the valleys of northern California and on the grassy plains of Oregon and Washington, the similar but fewer-petaled western buttercup, *Ranunculus occidentalis,* is the usual species. In the Saturnian days when the Indians lived entirely on the country, buttercup seeds were an important item in their diet. In May, after the blossoms had fallen and the seeds were set, the Indian women would sweep the ripened clusters with their long-handled gathering baskets, winnow out the acrid little seeds, and transferring them to a tray with hot pebbles or embers toss all about until the seeds were well parched when they would be ground to meal and eaten either so or made into mush or bread. The parching had the effect of dissipating the disagreeable pungency of the raw seeds, and according to one who has tested the matter gave a taste like that of parched corn.

CHAPTER XIV

*Of Dodecatheon, the Shooting Star, and How It
Came by Its Name; of Evening Primroses, Includ-
ing Some That Bloom by Day; of Godetia; and
How John Muir Breakfasted on Honey from the
California Fuchsia.*

W HEN the Reverend John Bannister, that "very
erudite man and consummate botanist," more than two
and a quarter centuries ago sent to England, from
Virginia wilds, for the garden of my Lord Bishop of
London, specimens of the pretty flower the world now
calls *Dodecatheon Meadia*, everybody took it to be just
another variety of primrose or cowslip, for obviously
it was of that family. So it was naturally called American cowslip. A generation passed, and Mark Catesby, an
English naturalist who spent several years in the southern colonies, discovered the same plant, and about 1743
was instrumental in introducing it into general cultivation abroad. At the same time he gave it a distinctive
name, *Meadia*, bestowed in honor of his friend and
patron, Dr. Richard Mead, a former London physician.
Now this Dr. Mead was a man far ahead of his time in
many respects, addicted to alarming heresies and, what
was worse, very outspoken about them. He tried, for
instance, to tell his orthodox time that when the Scrip-
tures speak of people possessed of devils, perhaps the
poor creatures were merely insane or epileptic. Among
other revolutionary ideas, he advocated inoculation

132

against pestilential diseases, and even persuaded the royal family, I read, to submit to it. He was an associate of Sir Isaac Newton, Dr. Samuel Johnson, Alexander Pope, and similar disturbers of the peace of solid eighteenth-century citizens. It was all quite scandalous, and the thought of such a dangerous fellow's having his name perpetuated by a beautiful flower that seemed destined to be a fixture in the gardens of Europe is said to have resulted in pressure being brought to bear on Linnæus, the botanical mogul of the day, to put a quietus on the name Meadia. However that may be, it is certain that Linnæus, in his *Species Plantarum*, published in 1753 and now accepted as the starting point of botanical nomenclature, did arbitrarily suppress Meadia as a genus, and for it substituted *Dodecatheon*, adding *Meadia* as a specific name, that is *Dodecatheon Meadia*.

With the opening up of the plant treasures of our great west, the wider range of Dodecatheon came to be realized. Instead of being confined, as was thought, to the Atlantic seaboard from Pennsylvania to Georgia, it was from time to time reported farther and farther westward—to Texas, the Mississippi Valley, the prairies of the northwest, the Rocky Mountains, and the shores of the Pacific. David Douglas was enthusiastic about it and wrote of it as imparting a grace to the verdure of the American spring "that can only be equaled by the European daisy or the common primrose." While it was apparent that in the western plants there was more or less variation from the Atlantic seaboard type, it was for a long time considered that this implied nothing more than varieties of one species. This view has been broken down, so that the original *Dodecatheon Meadia* is today considered limited to the eastern side of the continent, and the Pacific coast plants are regarded as easily a dozen distinct species. All are so uniform in their floral make-up, however, that even the novice recognizes a Dodecatheon at a glance. The bunched stamens pointed well forward from the corolla with petals streaming backward suggest a falling star, and make the popular name, shooting star, a particularly happy one. Another common name, wild cyclamen, from a resemblance to the true cyclamen, is also good, for the latter is of the same family. And for the sentimental there is lover's dart.

A high-mountain species, the large crimson-flowered *D. Jeffreyi*, has the distinction of having quickened the interest of the horticultural world in the tribe. Seeds of this species were sent from the Rocky Mountains to England, at about the close of our Civil War, and by the end of the century garden lists bristled with the names of cultivated forms of Dodecatheon, ranging in color from pure white through many a delicate shade of lilac and rose all the way to crimson. Among the more lowland species, there are two that fairly well divide California between them. One is *D. Hendersonii*, commemorating Prof. L. F. Henderson of Oregon, who first called the attention of Dr. Gray to its peculiarities. It is indigenous to the northern half of the state, where the name mosquito-bills obtained for it among the children. The other is *D. Clevelandii*, a lovely winter-blooming species of southern mesas and hillsides, its presence often betrayed by the pervading spicy fragrance of the flowers before the eye captures sight of them—a fragrance, by the way, that persists even in the dried blossom. The botanical name preserves the memory of a veteran botanist of San Diego, Daniel Cleveland, who died in

1929. His name is perpetuated in a number of other beautiful flowers of southern California which he brought to light.

The story of the word Dodecatheon has an interest of its own. Non-botanists complain today of the hard names that science insists on giving to the simplest flowers, but modern nomenclature is mild compared with that in use up to the time of Linnæus. Often those old names consisted of a cumbersome string of half a dozen words or more in Greek and Latin, and one of Linnæus's great services was to introduce a system by which each name was reduced to two words. Now, in putting this system into practice, he was like a man picking over a scrap pile for things utilizable. Looking about for a new name for Meadia, he found Dodecatheon to his hand, a word which is Greek for "twelve gods" and had been used by Pliny to designate some flower (what one we do not now know) that was of such beauty as to symbolize in itself the splendor of all the greater gods, of whom the Romans reckoned twelve. Our shooting star hardly does that, but perhaps Linnæus's specimen had twelve blossoms and buds upon its stalk, for such is not uncommonly the case, and that would have been reason enough to his methodical mind for adopting the name.[1]

Of the Evening Primrose family abundant in the Western United States, there are many interesting Pacific coast representatives—first of all, the evening primroses themselves, or Oenotheras. Best known is the old-fashioned *Oenothera biennis* formerly believed to have been distributed throughout the United States, though nowadays the forms indigenous west of the Rockies are

[1]Wittstein: *Etymologisch-botanisches Wörterbuch.*

counted as one distinct species, *O. Hookeri*. The eastern
plant was introduced into Europe two or three centuries
ago, where it has run wild and become a common weed.
It was upon one of its supposed varieties of garden
origin (*Lamarckiana*), as well as upon typical *O.
biennis*, that the Dutch biologist DeVries some years
ago conducted the experiments since become famous, in
support of the hypothesis of mutation as a means of
evolution—that is, by sudden change—rather than by
an imperceptible change over a long period. Europeans
have also introduced the species into their kitchen
gardens, for the sake of the large edible root, which may
be cooked like salsify or served raw as a salad.

Our Pacific coast plant was among Douglas's collections, and remained unnamed until christened by Torrey
and Gray in their *Flora of North America*. Though the
authors did not specifically say so, the assumption is the
name commemorates the eminent British botanist Sir
William Jackson Hooker, who placed Douglas's specimens at their service. It loves to sink its roots in damp
meadows and the moist borders of streams—a coarse,
rank-growing plant three or four feet tall, with bright
yellow flowers, three inches or more across. It is also
common in waste places about many rural settlements,
so that unsentimental country folk put it down as a
weed and little regard it. Apropos of this, Dr. Coville
has recorded a disrespectful legend of the Klamath
Indians[1] as to its origin. It seems that a long time ago,
when the animals associated and talked with men,
Coyote, who was a great braggart, met one day an
Indian divinity, who was very powerful and could do
anything he had a mind to—could make flowers, things

[1]*Contrib. U. S. National Herbarium*, Vol. v: 2.

to eat, anything. "That's nothing," said Coyote, "I can do those things, too." "Very well," said the god, "go ahead and make a flower." Coyote was taken aback by this unexpected challenge, for he knew in his heart that he could not make much of anything; but he slunk a little way off in the grass and disgorged his breakfast. In a little while this big, rank weed came up—the best this smart coyote could do. Nevertheless, when flowering time comes, it is nothing to be ashamed of. At sunset of summer evenings, the unfolding of the buds makes a delightful motion picture. Under the watcher's very eyes the calyx splits and falls apart, the corolla little by little swells, untangles its golden petals one from another, until at last the flower flashes out in the dusk full blown. "The leap of buds into ripe flowers," is the way Keats poetizes the event. All night the flower glows like the ghost of a miniature sun, but with returning day closes and withers.

If this lovely flower suggests the sun, its sister, *Oenothera trichocalyx* of the deserts, with pale round face, is as the moon. Its fragrant blooms are of the same generous size, but white, opening in late afternoon to last the night through and close early next morning, their whiteness at the last suffused with rose. The plant itself is clump-like with a number of shortish stems produced from a common short trunk. These become woody in age, curve upward, and their leafless tips, meeting, form a kind of skeletonized football, which eventually breaks away, and, kicked about by the wind, carries the seeds hither and yon. Incidentally, it becomes a baffling puzzle to the amateur botanist. Carl Lumholtz, in *New Trails in Mexico*, states that the green, juicy herbage is much relished by horses and cattle, and on the sand dunes near the head of the Gulf of California, where the plant is abundant, stock will be pastured on it for as much as three months and thrive absolutely without water. Indians, too, have learned its nutritiousness, and boil and eat the plants.

Evening Primroses, remarks Reginald Farrer somewhere, are as "polymorphous as a range of clouds at sunset," and in spite of their name are not all night bloomers. In fact, the majority stultify their vernacular name by being diurnal. Among them are the charming, bright little flowers popularly known as suncups—a name loosely applied to two or three species. *Oenothera bistorta* is abundant in sandy places throughout southern California, and besides the pleasure of its sunny flowers hugging the ground, there is the charm of its odd little twisted seed vessels, strung along the stem in the trail of the blossom. This coiling peculiarity is shared by some other species, notably the beach primrose (*O. spiralis*), a more or less prostrate perennial common on dunes and sea beaches from one end of the California coast to the other. The suncup of the northern half of the state is *O. ovata*, also called Golden Eggs, which bears its long-tubed flowers in great profusion from a rosette of wavy margined leaves flat to the ground, slightly beneath which the seed vessels are buried. The name Oenothera holds a mystery in itself. Its Greek root is the word for wine, and the name comes to us from Hellenic writers of twenty-odd centuries ago who applied it to some problematical plant, the roots of which appear to have been used to perfume wine, or to give it an added appeal to jaded palates.

Close akin to the Evening Primroses—so close, indeed, as to have been included in the same genus with them by the older botanists—is Godetia, named for a Swiss botanist, Charles H. Godet, who died half a century ago. There are a score of recognized species, all of the Pacific coast, beginning to brighten dry roadside banks and hillsides with their lovely bloom as spring draws to its close. Several of the species are popularly called farewell-to-spring. Dr. Jepson, who records the name rather grudgingly in his "Manual," drily adds that it is the invention "of some poet or other, as Herodotus would say." It may be so, but the poet, I think, must have been Spanish; for some of the Californians of my acquaintance in Santa Barbara County heard the flower called *Adiós, primavera*, that is, Farewell, spring, when they were children, which would carry the existence of the term as far back as the early 1860's at least. Sometimes, I am told, the form would be lengthened to *Última flor de primavera*, last flower of spring, or shortened to a tender *adiós*. My neighbor the Professor, who has his poetical moments, likes to think of the abbreviated form as the response of the flower itself (invested in his mind with personality) as if one said, "*Adiós, última flor de primavera, adiós*." "*Adiós*," echoes the flower. And the curtain descends.[1] But whatever may be said of the expression, I learn that at least in Santa Barbara County a common name for the flower was, and still is, *vara de*

[1]Mr. L. F. Ruiz of Santa Barbara, to whom I am indebted for much information about Spanish-Californian names and usages, states that in the mouths of the older generation one of the commonest expressions when spring is ending and the feel of approaching summer is in the air, is, "*Adiós, primavera.*" Farewell, spring. As the Godetia is at that season a common wayside flower throughout much of California, the term would naturally enough attach itself to it.

San José, St. Joseph's staff, the same that is universal among Spanish Americans for the hollyhock. The slender, upright stem of Godetia with rosy blossoms strung close upon it, one above another, naturally suggests a miniature hollyhock.

Douglas introduced several species of Godetia into England, among them the exquisite *G. amoena* (that is, the charming) which under cultivation has become the mother and grandmother of a host of forms, double as well as single, and in various shades of color. On its native hills, near the coast from Monterey to British Columbia, it blooms in lilac or crimson, often with a deeper tone at the base. *G. grandiflora*, a superb large-flowered sort, also of the coastal region of northern California, has developed some magnificent garden strains, the flowers in certain varieties as much as five inches across, and borne in dense clusters. An English nurseryman's catalogue that reached me not long ago listed twenty-nine different varieties of Godetia presumably developed from the two species just mentioned, the colors including cherry red, shell pink, rose, mauve, crimson, lavender, scarlet and pure white. A beautiful species mostly of the southern part of California, often seen in the chaparral or on shady banks, is *G. Bottae*, with rosy, purple-dotted flowers, discovered in 1829 by one M. P. E. Botta, a plant collector for the Musée de l'Histoire Naturelle of Paris, which explains the queer specific name.

Also of the Evening Primrose family is that tall, willowy plant the fireweed, so called because it springs up so frequently in the wake of forest fires. Increasing by means of underground horizontal rootstocks as well as by its tufted air-borne seeds, it spreads a purple mantle of bloom over the blackened ground—beauty for ashes. *Epilobium angustifolium,* botanists call it, and it is one of the world's most widely disseminated wild flowers, being found throughout much of northern North America, Europe and parts of Asia. In England it is known, curiously enough, as French or Persian willow because of its willow-like leaves and a popular belief that it is there of foreign origin. Robinson recommends it for introduction into rough shrubbery or copse, where it may bloom with the foxglove. In rocky ledges on the higher summits of northern California and the Nevada Mountains, *Epilobium obcordatum* has its home—a creeping, matted little plant bearing a profusion of bright rosy flowers, and happily called in the language of the people rock-fringe. Its value in the rock garden has long been recognized.

Also cultivated in rock gardens is the closely related California fuchsia, *Zauschneria californica* and its varieties—native to sandy arroyos, dry banks and rocky ridges, throughout central and southern California, thence skipping eastward to Nevada and Wyoming. The sprays of slender trumpet-like blossoms in vivid vermilion make a graceful note in the dun landscape of the latter year, and in low altitudes one often encounters them, last flowers of the old year, side by side with the New Year's firstlings. Zauschneria appears to have been first noted by the Bohemian Theodor Haenke, botanist with the Malaspina exploring expedition in search of the supposititious Northwest Passage, which touched upon the California coast in 1791. The plant was collected by him in the neighborhood of Monterey. After gathering dust in a herbarium for a generation, the dried specimens were described and named by another

Bohemian, Professor Presl of Prague, in honor of yet another Bohemian botanist, M. Zauschner. The flower was discovered again by Hartweg, who introduced it about 1847 into European gardens, where, if its roots be in sandy loam, it thrives in old, dry walls, or in the pockets of a sunny rock garden. Among the Spanish-speaking people of California the plant is called *balsaméa*, and, according to Mrs. Ida M. Blochman of Berkeley, who has made many contributions to our knowledge of the uses of the native flora by Spanish Californians, a wash made from it is regarded as efficacious for wounds and sores, especially for barbed-wire cuts on horses. John Muir found another use for it. In a letter to a friend describing a visit to the Kings River Cañon, he speaks of the exhaustion of his provisions, and breakfasting on the last day of his stay, on "crystal water, and air, and honey sucked from the scarlet flowers of Zauschneria, about one tenth as much as would suffice for a humming bird . . . wholly ungross and very nearly spiritual."[1]

[1] W. F. Badè: *Life and Letters of John Muir*, Vol. ii: 92.

CHAPTER XV

Of Some Aristocrats of the Cactus Family and One Black Sheep.

Aᴜɢᴜsᴛ 2, 1846. I looked in the direction of Bent's Fort and saw a huge United States flag flowing to the breeze, and straining every fiber of an ash pole planted over the center of a gate. The mystery was soon revealed by a column of dust to the east, advancing with about the velocity of a fast walking horse—it was 'the Army of the West.' I ordered my horses to be hitched up, and, as the column passed, took my place with the staff."

So begins Major W. H. Emory's "Notes of a Military Reconnaissance from Fort Leavenworth, in Missouri, to San Diego in California, made in 1846–7, with the advanced guard of the 'Army of the West.'" The war with Mexico was three months old, and the "Army of the West" was in motion with the object of taking forcible possession of the northern provinces of Mexico, more especially New Mexico and California. Emory, on that second of August, still a lieutenant, was a wide-awake young officer in charge of the corps of topographical engineers, and his racy notes upon the extraordinary features of the region traversed, which at that time was virtually a *terra incognita*, contain much interesting comment on the plant life of the southwest. Extensive collections of plants were made by Norman Bestor, assistant draughtsman of the expedition, and these were turned over for identification to Dr. John Torrey, the most eminent American botanist of that day. The collection proved noteworthy in numerous species new to science, and the memory of Emory is permanently enshrined in the botanical names given to many of them.

Among the notable plants thus brought to light, two are especially outstanding. One is the noble California fan-palm, first observed on November 29, 1846, near the head of Carriso Creek, at the eastern base of the California Cordilleras, as the mountain range between San Diego and the desert was then called. The trees were mistaken by the Emory party for Florida cabbage-palms. No specimens were collected, and it was reserved for a European botanist, thirty-three years later, to establish their true place in the botanical kingdom and give them the name by which they now go, Washingtonia, "in honor of the Great American," as the describer explained.

The other find was that very remarkable American tree, the saguaro or giant cactus, which Arizona has since adopted for her floral emblem. Just four weeks before encountering the California fan-palms, the expedition, while laboriously traveling the rough country of the upper Gila, had come upon a "cereus, six feet in circumference, and so high," writes Emory in his record of the incident, "that I could not reach half way to the top of it with the point of my sabre by many feet, and a short distance up the ravine is a grove of these plants, much larger than the one I measured, and with large branches. These plants bear a saccharine fruit much prized by the Indians and Mexicans. They are without leaves, the fruit growing to the boughs. The fruit

Carpenteria Californica

Fremontia Californica

Two of Frémont's discoveries

Owl's Clover (*Orthocarpus purpurascens*). White Sage across the road, at left

resembles the burr of a chestnut and is full of prickles, but the pulp resembles that of the fig, only more soft and luscious."

Continuing down the Gila to its mouth, the *pitahaya* (the Mexican name by which the expedition came to call it) was their frequent companion; and had they, on crossing into California, turned northward for fifteen or twenty miles on the west side of the Colorado River, it would have greeted them again. That particular region, however, between the Laguna Dam and Needles, is the only one in California where the Saguaro has so far been found to be indigenous. There it grows on stony mesas in a few scattered groups; so the margin is very narrow that permits California to claim any proprietorship in this "Goliath of the cacti," as Mr. J. Smeaton Chase calls it in his *California Desert Trails.*

Naturally, so unwieldy and prickly a subject baffles a collector of specimen material, and all that Emory carried back to the botanical world about it was a verbal description and a few tiny seeds. With only these, poor Dr. Engelmann, the famous cactologist and director of the Missouri Botanic Gardens, to whom it was submitted for determination, had to solve the puzzle of identity. Nevertheless, he made a plucky go of it, decided the giant was new to science, and called it *Cereus giganteus.* This name persisted unchallenged for more than half a century, until the Carnegie Desert Botanical Laboratory at Tucson came into being, when the plant was redubbed as *Carnegia gigantea,* in honor of the philanthropic patron of that institution of research. "Something nice had to be done for St. Andrew," observed my neighbor the Professor in a malicious aside, as we were discussing the subject one day. "All the same, the validity of the new name is not unanimously accepted, and you are still in good society if you say *Cereus gigantea.*"

Apropos of Dr. Engelmann, it speaks well for his perspicacity that in his published description he stated that although he found no record of the plant's being indigenous to California, he believed its presence there probable—thus anticipating the event by half a century. Its actual existence on California soil was discovered in March, 1905, by Dr. D. T. MacDougal in the course of exploration work for the lately established Desert Laboratory.

While Engelmann's description based on Emory's discovery is the first scientific recognition of this noble cactus, the plant had been casually referred to in the narration of some earlier travelers. Humboldt noted its existence; J. O. Pattie, an adventurer who crossed the southern deserts in 1825, saw it; and it must surely have been seen by the observant Spaniards during their sixteenth- and seventeenth-century *entradas* into the southwestern desert.

The saguaro ranges south into the Mexican state of Sonora, where it has long been of economic worth to the people, as it has been to the Papagos of southern Arizona. The reddish-purple fruit is eaten either raw or cooked, and is the source of an agreeable table syrup, as well as of an alcoholic beverage, whose consumption has long been an important feature in the ceremonies attending the Papago New Year, which dates from the saguaro harvest. The small seeds are a valuable by-product, and on being ground form a buttery paste that makes a luscious spread for aboriginal *tortillas*, or corn cakes. The large white blossoms are marvelous creations. Many cactus flowers are notably rich in stamens, but the saguaro's would seem to out-stamen them all. One inquisitive botanist has told us[1] that he had the stamens of a single flower counted, and they totaled 3,482, and the ovary of one pistil contained 1,980 incipient seeds. One would think with such productivity the desert would be one vast forest of saguaros, but as a matter of fact the birds see to it that relatively few seeds get a chance to germinate. Once started, however, the plants are long lived, and the larger ones, whose massive fluted columns rise sometimes to a height of thirty-five feet or more, may be as much as two centuries old and weigh six or eight tons. So the wise ones say.

Not only alive, but in death also the saguaro has from time immemorial been a boon to the desert dwellers. When the dead trunk falls and the dried integument shrinks away, a skeleton of slender wooden rods is left, which are useful just as wooden rods from the planing mill are useful. The Papagos employ them for poles to dislodge the saguaro fruit from tall plants, and for reinforcing the mud walls of their houses, just as the prehistoric cliff dwellers did centuries before them.

As a final virtue I will add that as a lodging house, the saguaro is in prime favor with the woodpeckers, which tunnel their way into it, creating a safe hiding place for their nests. Hardly a trunk or limb but bears several round holes marking the entrances to their nests, which are later often occupied by other birds, fly catchers, pigmy owls, and so on, shameless sorts without pride of architecture and content with others' leavings. The walls of these excavations, which may be a foot deep

[1] Chas. E. Bessey in *Science*, n. s. 40: 680.

and four or five inches in diameter, soon harden and remain intact after the death of the saguaro, resembling empty pitchers or vases. They are then easily picked out, and the canny Papagos collect them and use them for *ollas*.

On the California deserts no member of the cactus family, aside from the saguaro, which not one in ten thousand ever sees there, is more interesting to the casual observer than the Biznaga, the barrel or hedgehog cactus (*Echinocactus cylindraceus*, or as Britton and Rose in their monumental work *Cactaceae* prefer to call it, *Ferocactus acanthodes*). Its stout, barrel-shaped body, sometimes as tall as a tall man, is vertically furrowed and ridged like the pleats of an accordion, and upon its summit in the spring is borne a chaplet of pale yellow flowers. It is a most benevolent cactus; even its spines, which are manifold, are much less vicious than those of the general run of its kindred. Beautiful spines, they are, transversely barred, creamy yellow and pink; faintly musical, if you twang them with your finger, serviceable, indeed, as phonograph needles. Not long ago at a desert ranch-house, I heard Schubert's Unfinished Symphony played on a phonograph with a needle made from a spine clipped by my host from a near-by Biznaga. Walt Whitman once wrote a poem on Italian music in Dakota. Had he known this musical cactus he might have written another.

This plant also occurs in Lower California, and either of it or of a kindred species (for there are many species of the same genus distributed throughout our southwest and northern Mexico) the Jesuit historian Clavigero records that the spines were sometimes straightened out and used at the Lower California missions as knitting needles! One's fancy is touched by the picture of some poor padre of the ancient day sitting in the chimney corner of his mission of a winter's night, seeking to achieve a pair of stockings with such clumsy make-shifts.[1]

The star rôle of the Biznaga, however, is as a water barrel in a thirsty land. The juice of most cactuses is bitter and slimy, too disagreeable for a man to stomach, but the watery content of the Biznaga is quite drinkable. An individual on the sunny side of middle age makes the best subject. The top is sliced across and removed, and the juicy interior, resembling the pulp of an unripe watermelon, is pounded until the resultant bowl-like cavity is filled with liquid, which may then be dipped up with cupped hands—or a tin cup, if you are fastidious. It has something of a vegetable tang, and is much more palatable than a good deal of the water that travelers on the desert must put up with. As a drink from a Biznaga means the mutilation of the plant, nothing short of necessity warrants cutting into one, and county ordinances have been passed in recent years making it a punishable offense to collect or destroy these remarkable creations on public lands, except by express permission of the authorities and for scientific purposes. In old times the ingenious Indians, besides plundering the Biznaga of its water, utilized the plant

[1]The word *biznaga* is commonly used in Mexico for any one of several species of globular or cylindric cactus, and according to the Mexican scholar Don Cecilio A. Robelo in his *Dictionary of Aztequisms* (Cuernavaca, 1904) is derived from the Aztec term *huitznáhuac*, meaning "surrounded by spines." According to the same authority the Aztecs employed *biznaga* spines to draw blood from the victims of their sacrificial rites. Because of this the plant acquired a sacred association.

itself as a cooking vessel. First burning the spines off, they scooped out a large part of the inside pulp, from which the water was squeezed, put back, and then heated by the usual aboriginal process of dropping hot stones into it. Thus the food was cooked. These crude boilers were sometimes found at abandoned camp sites of the natives by early American exploring parties. So Dr. J. M. Bigelow has recorded in the account of the Whipple Expedition dispatched by the United States government to scout out a route for a Pacific railway.[1]

Commonest of all the California cactuses are the various species of the genus Opuntia, the so-called Prickly Pears. They occur in two distinct forms—one with cylindrically jointed branches, and the other with flattened pad-like joints. Of the former the most famous —or, perhaps better said, infamous—is *Opuntia Bigelovii*, which often covers extensive areas on both the Mohave and Colorado deserts of California, thence eastward to Nevada and Arizona. Its first appearance in the annals of science was in 1854, recorded by that Dr. Bigelow of the Whipple Expedition, just mentioned. Let us listen to the Doctor's account, and if you have traveled the desert either afoot or horseback, you will not be in doubt as to the plant he speaks of.

The party is descending the Bill Williams Fork of the Colorado River in Arizona, and is nearing the California border. "We find," he writes under date of February 7th, "a new species of Opuntia with a reticulated woody stem very fragile at the joints before hardening into wood, and armed with spines worse than those of the porcupine. It is called by the Mexicans '*chug*.' The plant is the horror of man and beast.

[1]Pacific Railroad Reports, Vol. iv: 12.

Our mules are as fearful of it as ourselves. The barbed spines stick so fast in the flesh, that the joint of the plant is separated from the main stem before the spines can be withdrawn." What these Mexicans called it, however, was not *chug*, I think, but *choya*, or, as the Spanish write it, *cholla*, the name they give it today. In honor of the discoverer it was given botanical standing as *Opuntia Bigelovii*. In appearance it is a very striking plant and unmistakable. A short trunk, to which dead and blackened spines give a sinister look, is surmounted by a dense head of intricate branches composed of swollen joints rather larger than chestnut burs, and densely covered with spines of a deceitful beauty but ferocious efficiency. Each spine, delicately and minutely barbed, is neatly encased for some inscrutable reason in a whitish, papery sheath that glistens like silver in the sun. Touch with your finger the tip of a spine and instantly the barb is fastened firmly in your flesh; the lightest pull on your part and off comes the bristling joint; you shake your smarting finger to rid yourself of the incubus, only to wince with pain. If you keep your head you realize that any attempt to dislodge the clinging bur with your other hand would merely entangle that; so you put your captive hand to the ground, and holding down the bur with your foot pull loose your finger, bleeding and throbbing with pain, to find that in all likelihood the devilish thing has thrust its barb through shoe leather into your foot. Do you wonder that Dr. Hornaday dubbed it "Bigelow's accursed choya"? Bad as your plight is, your animals are in a worse, for they are helpless to rid themselves of the pest. If you have nothing better at hand, you may improvise a forceps of two sticks to pull it loose.

The experienced desert horse or mule has learned enough botany to recognize *Opuntia Bigelovii* on sight and tries to give it a wide berth, though the fallen burs, which clutter the ground about the plants, add to the complexity of the poor beast's problem.

Yet the devil is entitled to his due. Under the protection of the terrible, intricate branches, the cactus wren marvelously builds her nest in the midst of them, darts in and out without accident to her trig little body, and eventually launches her brood safely on the voyage of life out of this den of wicked spines. Moreover, after the soft tissue of trunk and branch has shriveled away, the woody skeleton of the plant is exposed in the form of a hollow cylinder, with regularly disposed meshes, material for curio makers. Impecunious health seekers in the desert, on whose hands time hangs heavy, are helped temporarily to forget their troubles and to add a bit to their dwindling store of money by making canes, napkin rings, picture frames and what-not from the skeletons of this and kindred species.

This same Whipple Expedition turned up another cactus very common on the deserts, which belongs to the flat jointed section of Opuntia, and which Dr. Bigelow found in the same region with the vicious *cholla*. Arizonans call it beaver-tail, from the smooth flat spineless pads that remotely suggest the tail of that animal—a good enough vernacular name which Californians might do worse than adopt. The plant grows in low, spreading clumps, a few inches high, and in the spring, when covered with masses of rosy flowers wide open to the sun, few sights are prettier. Dr. Engelmann christened it *Opuntia basilaris*, because the joints originate from a common base, forming a kind of rosette. **Dr. Coville**, botanist of the Death Valley expedition in 1891, observed that the Panamint Indians utilized this cactus as an important source of food. In late spring, when the plant is fat with juice, the fleshy joints or pads, and their buds, flowers and fruit, would be garnered in baskets, each piece carefully rubbed with grass to remove the fine prickles (with which the plant is annoyingly supplied in lieu of spines), and then spread in the sun. When thoroughly dry, the plant keeps indefinitely and would be prepared for consumption by boiling. Instead of sun-drying, another process sometimes followed was to steam the fresh plants for a day in a pit heated with hot stones and covered with earth.

The seeds of the Opuntia fruits were very generally used by the California Indians as food, being first ground into meal and boiled as mush. By the Mexican population the juicy fruits, "prickly pears," of certain flat jointed sorts—as the varieties of *O. occidentalis*, common to the valleys and coast of southern California, are called *tunas*, and when thoroughly ripe are palatable to anybody. There is a trick, however, in preparing them, for they are dotted with detestable little clumps of tiny bristles, very irritating to the flesh that touches them. First of all these must be removed by careful brushing, as with a bunch of dry grass or California sage (*limpia-tuna*, that is *tuna* cleaner, is the name Mexicans give to plants customarily so used). Then with a knife the two ends of the *tuna* are thinly sliced off; and lastly, a longitudinal cut is made down the thickish rind, which can then be laid neatly back, releasing the luscious pulp in a compact mass. Though seedy, it will be found of good flavor and refreshing.

Among the Mexicans, the flat jointed Opuntias are known as *nopal*, and thereby hangs a tale, as familiar to Mexican children as the story of Columbus is to ours. The word, it seems, is the Aztec *nopalli*, a trifle worn down by use, and the plant as well as its name is interwoven with the legendary history of Mexico. Five centuries or so before the Spanish conquest, the Aztecs made their appearance in the valley of Mexico, unwelcome intruders among a people who had long occupied the land and had no use for foreigners. For several generations the newcomers led a nomad existence, battling their way from pillar to post, and even enduring slavery at one period, until on a day in what students of the Aztec calendar believe to be the year 1325, they came to a halt on the marshy borders of a great lake. There upon a branching *nopal*, springing from a rock jutting up from the water, was perched a great eagle with wings spread to the sun, and fast in his beak a writhing serpent. The Aztec leaders hailed it as a sign that here the people's wanderings should cease, and on pilings sunk in the swamp was begun the building of their capital Tenochtitlan—the place of the *tuna*—upon whose site stands the present city of Mexico. You will see the incident depicted in the modern Mexican coat-of-arms, and repeated on the national flag—a device that is, as a matter of fact, an adaptation from the Aztec hieroglyph for the ancient capital of the Montezumas.

Just what species of *nopal* that mythical eagle perched upon we shall probably never know, but as two kinds introduced into California by the Franciscan Fathers, and now more or less naturalized near the old California missions (*O. megacantha* and *O. ficus-indica*), are known to have been cultivated as fruit trees in pre-Cortesian Mexico, either might fit the story. Both were alike useful in the early history of California. The plants themselves served several purposes. As a hedge nothing was more effective; the tender young joints, or *pencas*, as they were called, as innocent of spines as a baby is of whiskers, were cut up and cooked as a vegetable; while the mature pads, split longitudinally and soaked, made a homely sort of poultice for bruises, or were boiled and crushed for the sake of the gummy juice which stiffened mortar and added adhesiveness to the white-wash on adobe walls. But to the Indian mind the crowning touch was the fruit—those ruddy or golden *tunas*, larger and juicier than any the native California species produced. So delicately did they tickle the palates of aboriginal and Californian alike that they have entered into the proverbs of the people. One I heard not long ago. *Al nopal vienen solo cuando tiene tunas*, it runs—People visit the cactus only when the fruit is on it. The saying's general applicability is obvious: If we have nothing to give, who will visit us?

CHAPTER XVI

Of the Mountain Lilacs and How You May Wash Your Hands with Their Blossoms; and of Their Cousin the Sacred Bark.

Among the most cheerful sights of a California spring is the blooming of the Ceanothus—the mountain or California lilac of common speech, or, as others prefer to call it, oddly enough, myrtle. From one end of the state to the other, and from the seacoast to a mile or more above tide, this characteristic shrub of the chaparral in some of its many forms spreads sheets of fragrant bloom in blue, lavender or shining white, on mountain slopes and cañon sides and open ridges. Indeed, one need not wait for it until spring, for in the milder parts of its range there are species in full flower as early as January. The dainty blossoms, borne in multitudinous plumy spikes and trusses, are individually very small, and of an unusual form, best observed under a pocket lens. The petals are hood-shaped with a relatively long claw, suggesting a Lilliputian bonnet on a stick, or, as the late George B. Sudworth, government dendrologist, saw it, "a minute tobacco pipe." The flowers of most species, if not all, have the peculiar property of producing an abundant and cleansing lather when rubbed up in water, a fact that was known to the aborigines. The same is more or less true of leaves, bark and green seed vessels, but the result is less satisfactory.

Another name, soap-bush, for Ceanothus has originated from this surprising quality, an exhibition of which never fails to delight novices in plant ways.

One of the oldest known, if not the very earliest discovered, of the California lilacs, is the blue-flowered *Ceanothus thyrsiflorus*, indigenous from Monterey County northward along the redwood belt to Oregon, sometimes graduating into the size of a small tree. It goes locally by several names, blue blossom and blue myrtle among them. I have read that specimens of it were among the indefatigable Menzies's collections, which remained for so many years neglected and unnamed in various European herbaria. That Dr. Eschscholtz whose memory Chamisso insured to posterity by naming the California poppy for him gave this Ceanothus the specific name by which we know it and published its description in 1820. In those days it formed dense thickets at the northern end of the peninsula where San Francisco now stands. It is one of the most ornamental of the genus, evergreen and blossoming from March to May, and when the early American settlers would clear a bit of land for a house site, the beauty of this charming plant would cause them often to leave specimens near, as door-yard shrubs. It is of record that some of those veterans were still standing as late as the 1870's.[1]

Hardly less charming is the species *integerrimus*—the very pure—common at middle altitudes in the Sierra Nevada and Coast ranges, as well as the higher parts of the southern California mountains. The flowers are usually white, but sometimes assume shades of pale blue or even pink. When with the mellowing year and

[1] E. L. Greene in *Garden and Forest*, Vol. v: 239.

the approach of the snow upon the upper peaks and
ridges the deer retreat to lower pastures, they find an
acceptable browse in the leaves and spicy twigs of this
Ceanothus, and so mountain folk call it deer-bush.
Cattlemen have come to prize it for their herds when
other forage fails. Denizen of similar situations is the
well known *C. cordulatus*, a depressed, flattish white-
flowered, thorny shrub, two or three feet high and
sometimes as much as eight or nine across, interlocking
in neighborly fellowship with others of its kind, until
there results such an impenetrable barrier to progress
that even sheep are given pause. It has acquired the
popular name snow-brush, which Mr. George Hansen,
of Amador County, California, writing in *Garden and
Forest* a generation ago, attributed to the sheep men
of that time, who, driving their flocks into the upper
elevations in June, when snow was still to be encountered, could hardly distinguish at a distance the low
wide-spreading masses of this shrub, then in snowy
flower, from lingering snow banks. Others maintain
that the name is from that characteristic flattened
shape, which is claimed to be a result of the pressure
of the snow mass lying packed on top of the shrub for
months at a stretch, often to the depth of twelve to
fifteen feet.

A naturally prostrate Ceanothus is *C. prostratus*.
With densely matted branches, it makes a compact,
evergreen ground cover in the coniferous woods of the
northern half of California northward to Washington,
covered in flower with a film of deep blue. It is an
abundant species on the shores of Lake Tahoe and in
the Yosemite region. To this plant the mountain children have given the name squaw-carpet or mahala

mats—terms that are synonymous, as the word Mahala is a common designation for an Indian woman. The reason for this association of the plant with the aborigines I have not learned, but Dr. F. V. Coville, in a paper entitled "Notes on Plants Used by the Klamath Indians,"[1] states that while the members of that tribe make no use of the plant, it enters pleasantly into their folklore. It seems, according to their myths, that in the old days when the birds and animals lived like men, the hawk employed the leaves of this Ceanothus for his arrowheads; and so in the language of the Klamath it goes by a word signifying "hawk-arrowhead-plant." And, indeed, the thick coarsely toothed leaves are not dissimilar in appearance to an arrowpoint of a kind. Dr. Hall has recorded that Indians and stockmen of Butte and Plumas counties make a decoction of the roots and bruised leaves as a blood purifier and a remedy for kidney troubles.

Of all the forty-odd species and varieties of Ceanothus indigenous to California the most abundant and widespread, to quote Dr. Jepson, is *C. cuneatus*, the so-called buck-brush. Its rather small, thick leaves, wedge shaped at base (*cuneatus* means that), are set opposite each other on the stem, an arrangement not usual in Ceanothus, for in the majority of cases you will find the leaves alternately disposed. It loves the company of its kind and forms impenetrable thickets, sometimes square miles in extent, on dry rocky mountain slopes from the Columbia River in Oregon to Lower California, a gray-green mantle most of the year, but for a brief space in spring breaking into creamy white from a myriad flowers. So thoroughly does this shrub dominate

[1]*Contrib. U. S. Nat. Herb.* Vol. v: 2.

the chaparral of certain sections of the state that it has taken to itself the word chaparral, and by that name in such localities the shrub itself is called. It is a prolific and ready seeder, springing quickly up again in the wake of the pioneer's clearing implements and earning the mountain rancher's pronounced disfavor.

You may be sure that the beauty of the Ceanothus did not escape the attention of the early collectors on the Pacific coast for European gardens and nurseries. Douglas, Hartweg, Lobb and doubtless others introduced species after species into England during the first decades of the nineteenth century; and according to William Robinson, six or eight of them are today cherished subjects in English gardens, where they are grown preferably as wall shrubs, since they are rather sensitive to wintry weather over there. Before the introduction of the California species abroad, however, France had received from Mexico a delightful blue-flowered species, *Ceanothus azureus*, which was to have a marked influence upon Ceanothus culture in Europe, and eventually in America. Under cultivation it developed the famous variety *Gloire de Versailles*, a form even more beautiful than the type. This, when crossed with the very hardy *C. americanus*, a species native to the Atlantic coast of North America, which had been introduced into England as early as 1713 (being in fact the species on which Linnæus founded the genus Ceanothus[1]), there came into being a series

[1]One wonders in vain what was the reason for this inexplicable name. It dates back to the old Greek naturalists who gave it to some now forgotten plant and could by no means have had anything to do with the North American genus of shrubs of the name. Perhaps the only explanation is this: Linnæus seems to

WILD IRIS (*Iris Missouriensis*), Inyo County, California

FUCHSIA-FLOWERED GOOSEBERRY

PINK-FLOWERING
CURRANT

of charming hybrids. Most of these have originated in French and Belgian nurseries. Besides *C. americanus*, another hardy American, *C. ovatus*, occurring through the Mississippi Valley southward to Texas, has served sometimes as one parent. These two species, by the way, have played a minor rôle in the drama of American history, the dried leaves having been used as a poor substitute for Chinese tea in two wars—*americanus* during the Revolution, and *ovatus* (according to Ellen D. Schultz in *Texas Wild Flowers*) during our Civil War. Doubtless some of the Pacific coast species would serve as well, since astringency, a desideratum of a certain class of tea drinkers, is a characteristic of the botanical family to which Ceanothus belongs.

Until comparatively recently the value of the native Ceanothus as a garden subject in California was virtually overlooked, but thanks principally to the efforts of Mr. Theodore Payne, the veteran plantsman of Los Angeles, who has worked for years to gain recognition for native material in Pacific coast gardens, many species are now seen in our cultivated grounds. Their billowy clouds of blossom in white and blue and lavender make an exquisite show in the spring, worth traveling far to see. Intensest blue of all is *C. cyaneus* (i.e., dark blue), which was unknown until a dozen years ago, when Miss Myrtle Philbrook discovered it on a rocky hilltop near Lakeside, San Diego County. Its lateness of blooming—the latter part of May or early June, after other species are over—together with the richer

have had a way of making a sort of grab bag of unrecognizable names used by the ancients, and when at a loss for a name for a new plant, he probably put in his hand and drew one out at random. So one time, perhaps, came Ceanothus to hand.

color of its flower masses and the brilliancy of foliage, marked it at once as a desirable addition to gardens. The story of its naming is interesting. An autochrome picture of the novelty was sent by Miss K. O. Sessions, the noted plantswoman of San Diego, to Miss Alice Eastwood of the California Academy of Sciences, who realized it was a new species and named it at once from the picture. The formal "baptism of science" was not given until two years later, when Miss Eastwood received specimens and published a verbal description.

Most species of Ceanothus are rather readily propagated from seed, though in particular instances a knowledge of the conditions under which the subject grows in nature is essential. Prof. Howard E. McMinn, of Berkeley, who has specialized in the genus, had a curious experience with the seeds of the rare *C. purpureus* (*C. Jepsonii*). After repeated failures, he conceived the idea of soaking them first in ice water in a refrigerator for several days, thus re-creating conditions to which the seeds (they are shed in the autumn) are exposed on the Napa County mountain ridge, chilled in winter by cold rains and snow, the one known locality for the species in nature. After this frosty treatment he got his seedlings. There are other species which are of a different temperament, and seedlings spring up abundantly after a brush fire. In propagating these some success has been had by burning leaves and so on over the seed bed, again taking a hint from nature.

Of the same family with Ceanothus (the *Rhamnaceae* or Buck-thorns) is the famous *Rhamnus californica*, the *cáscara sagrada* or sacred bark of the Spanish Californians, a variable and abundant shrub with natty evergreen foliage, occurring in many parts of California.

Its original title to fame lay in the medicinal value of its smooth dark gray bark, a decoction of which was found to be both tonic and gently laxative. There is a tradition that the shrub got its name *cáscara sagrada* from the Franciscan missionaries, whose knowledge of its value, it is assumed, was communicated by their Indian neophytes. That may be so, but I find it significant that a nearly related European species, *Rhamnus cathartica*, was well known for similar properties (evidenced by the specific name) as far back as Linnæus's time; so that those early padres may well have discovered for themselves the plant's secret. From Mendocino County northward *cáscara sagrada* occurs as a tree sometimes thirty feet tall, with foliage regularly deciduous in the autumn, and by most botanists is regarded as a distinct species, *Rhamnus purshiana*. The stripping of the bark, which is a minor industry in Oregon and Washington, is naturally destructive of the trees above ground, but fortunately the stumps tend to send up vigorous sprouts, a hint from Nature that she is on the side of perpetuating the supply if man will do his part. This, I am told, he is not doing, but strips and strips, and devil take the future. In 1891 the tree was introduced into England, where in the mild southern and western counties it thrives happily enough, so that the desirability of growing it there commercially for the bark has sometimes been discussed. Among our northwestern bark strippers, this Rhamnus is frequently known, curiously enough, as Chittim or Shittim wood, which gives a sort of Biblical flavor to the business.

With its crown of clean, glossy green, full-veined leaves, *Rhamnus californica* makes an interesting garden subject and is cultivated both abroad and in California.

An especially attractive feature in autumn is furnished
by the berries, which are the size of small cherries,
clustered at the branch ends, and run a pretty gamut of
color; green, yellow, red, purple and even black berries
may be found at the same time on the same bush. So
does it handsomely make up for the negligible bloom of
spring, for the flowers are minute, yellowish-green
affairs, noticed mainly by the bees. These berries, in
spite of their bitterness, are particularly palatable to
the wild pigeons, whence the name pigeon-berry, heard
in some parts of California. Spanish Californians called
the plant *yerba del oso* (bear-weed), and sometimes used
the juice from the crushed berries as a remedy for Rhus-
poisoning, allowing it to dry on the patient's skin. The
seeds, too, have played a rôle in the plant's modest
drama. Oval of outline, flat on one side and convex on
the other, they have a certain likeness to grains of
coffee; and so another and more prevalent vernacular
name for the species, coffee-berry or wild coffee. The
resemblance, however, goes no further, though simple
people have tried to make a beverage of them—but
fruitlessly. Even the Indians, whose inventive genius
has found means of utilizing in their domestic economy
many an unpromising seed, seem to have found this nut
uncrackable, or at least not worth the cracking.

CHAPTER XVII

Of Dr. Darlington's Pitcher Plant and the Dar-winian Sundew; a Short Chapter but Curious.

WHEN the Wilkes Exploring Expedition sailed out of Hampton Roads on August 19, 1838, for its celebrated four years' cruise in Pacific waters, it carried as assistant botanist a young Scottish horticulturist, W. D. Bracken-ridge by name, whose destiny it was to bring to light one of the most notable of Pacific coast plants—*Darling-tonia californica.* Three years later the ships arrived at the mouth of the Columbia in Oregon, and a detach-ment of men was ordered to proceed south by land and meet the ships again at San Francisco. Brackenridge in his capacity of botanist accompanied the land party, and in some marshy land bordering a tributary of the upper Sacramento River, a few miles south of Mount Shasta, he made the discovery of this remarkable plant. Years afterward he told Thomas Meehan, the veteran nurseryman and botanist of Philadelphia, that the way it came about was this:

One day in his enthusiasm for botanizing he had strayed a considerable distance from his companions when he suddenly found himself confronted by a band of Indians whose appearance was anything but reassur-ing to him. He took to his heels and in his flight caught a glimpse of a plant so strikingly strange that he was sure it must be something new. Making a flying grab at it, he arrived in camp with a handful of queer-looking leaves and the remains of one seed vessel at the top of a dried stalk; but this was enough for Dr. Torrey, to whom the material was sent, to determine the plant's relationship, though not enough to fix it specifically. For years Torrey cherished the hope that a better specimen would come to his hand and enable him to complete the matter, and at last one did. In May, 1851, Dr. G. W. Hulse, an army surgeon with a botanical flair, as many of his kind had in those days, and whose name is preserved in the beautiful Pacific coast genus *Hulsea* of the Composite family, found the long desired plant in full flower in the same general neighborhood where Brackenridge had clutched his fistful of leaves a decade before.

The remarkable feature of the plant, the one that makes it really unique in our flora, is the character of the leaves. They are slender, inflated "pitchers" from one to three feet high, growing in an erect cluster. The top of each "pitcher" is shaped like a dome, mottled yellowish green, and pierced on the lower side by an opening more or less obscured by a couple of flaring purple-veined streamers suggesting a fish tail. Within, the "pitcher" near its mouth is sweet with a secretion very alluring to insects. Following the honeyed trail, the silly little bug arrives by and by at a region of smooth downward-pointing bristles over which he slides easily enough to find himself in the midst of an innumerable company of other deluded insects in a pool of liquid, which fills the bottom of the "pitcher" and is similar in property to gastric juice. Unable to return, he dies unhappily, and as much of him as is digestible is absorbed by the plant. The whole arrangement constitutes an ingenious natural fly-trap, and is a peculiarity of the Sarracenia or pitcher-plant family, of which this singular plant is a member. Its occurrence is limited to marshy meadows and sunny stream borders within a rather narrow geographical lane running diagonally from Plumas County, California, a distance of about a hundred and fifty miles, to the northwest corner of the state and a short way into Oregon. The purplish flowers, dark-veined, borne on tall stems and in evidence for a few weeks in the spring, are less noticeable than the curious leaves, whose conspicuous bald crowns have given rise to the local name, calf's-head.

Darlingtonia, the name that Torrey gave to the plant, was bestowed in honor, as he stated, of "one of the worthiest of American botanists," Dr. William Darlington, of West Chester, Pennsylvania, who, though he never visited California, gained more than a local reputation in the first half of the nineteenth century as the botanical historian of an interesting but restricted area. This region he immortalized for plant lovers in a delightful gossipy volume entitled *Flora Cestrica*, in which he described the wild plants of Chester County, Pennsylvania, with notes quaint, shrewd and curious on their history, uses and associations. Though he never saw his distinguished floral namesake in nature, he was privileged in his ripe old age to see and marvel over it in cultivation; for it has proved complaisant not only to greenhouse culture both in America and abroad, but has even been grown outdoors as far north on our Atlantic seaboard as New England, though that takes skillful management. In British bog gardens, William Robinson says, it is less trouble than under glass.

Also with a taste for insect meat, but differently

implemented for its capture and consumption, are the Droseras or Sundews, of which two or three species are indigenous on our Pacific coast. The round-leaved sundew, *D. rotundifolia*, is a quaint little thing of hairs and paddles, inhabiting mountain bogs of the northern part of California, and extending thence eastward to the Atlantic. Its small, reddish, broad-bladed leaves, disposed in rosettes flat to the earth, are fringed and stippled with bristles each of which poises at its tip a glistening drop of transparent gluey liquid. A gnat or fly alighting on the sticky leaf is held fast; immediately the stiff hairs bend down and, pinning the insect fast, secrete a digestive juice that gradually consumes such parts as the plant has stomach for. Sundews, of which there are a hundred species or so in the world, occur in almost every part of the globe, with a special predilection for Australia. The round-leaved sundew formerly had a great reputation in the Old World for curative and occult power. Ancient writers gravely assure us that it will, if carried in the pocket, protect the bearer from the craft of witches and ensure good friends; a drop of the juice in the stirrup cup will keep the rider fresh on the longest journey; and as for curing asthma and bronchitis, it had a reputation that lingers in some places, they say, to this day.

In Darwin's classic work on *Insectivorous Plants*, more than half the book is devoted to a circumstantial recital of his experiments with the round-leaved sundew. His attention had been attracted to some plants of it growing upon a heath in Sussex, and he was surprised to find that a great many flies and insects were being continually caught by the leaves. Not content with observing the actions of the plant toward the prey that came naturally within reach of its tentacles (as Darwin preferred to call the wicked little bristles) he plied his sundews with all sorts of substances—bits of meat, raw or cooked, specks of cartilage, albumen, gluten, droplets of milk, splinters of bone. The responsive little herb showed an interest in pretty much everything given it, but met its Waterloo when a crumb of cheese, one twentieth of a cubic inch in size, was placed on each paddle of a four-leafed specimen. The leaves turned up their edges as usual; the tentacles bent down over the prospective tidbit, pouring out their digestive juice; but though it had managed to extract something from as unpromising a subject as a splinter of bone, the cheese was too much for the gallant plant, which retired eventually from the contest with one leaf quite dead and several tentacles badly wounded!

CHAPTER XVIII

Of Yedra, the Poison Oak, and Its Well Behaved Sisters.

IN ALL woods and by every wayside there prospers an abominable shrub or weed, called poison oak, whose very neighborhood is venomous to some and whose actual touch is avoided by the most impervious." So wrote Robert Louis Stevenson in that idyl of central California, *The Silverado Squatters.* Half a century earlier the naturalists of Captain Beechey's exploring expedition to the Pacific encountered it in their botanizing jaunts in the region around San Francisco Bay, and its poisonous nature made so great an impression on the party that the official report of the voyage featured it as "the most remarkable shrub in the country." They carried specimens of it home to England, where it was grown in the gardens of the London Horticultural Society, and its picture in flower was reproduced in color in the *Botanical Register* as a noteworthy novelty. They found the Spanish-speaking population calling it, as they do today, *yedra,* which simply means "ivy." The Mexican, with his flair for the picturesque, has quaintly dubbed it *mala mujer* (that is, "bad woman") and sometimes *hincha-huevos,* which may be Englished as "swollen eggs," obviously suggested by the blisters it produces on the victim's skin.

The Pacific coast poison oak is very similar to the

eastern poison ivy (*Rhus radicans*), but critical examination reveals some small differences, mainly in the leaf outline. These have caused it to be classed as a distinct species, *R. diversiloba*, named from the diverse lobing of the three leaflets that make up the compound leaf and somewhat resemble the foliage of certain species of California oaks. As one species or another, sometimes in the form of a shrub, sometimes as a climbing vine, this marvelous plant spreads itself across the continent from the Atlantic to the Pacific and from Canada to Mexico. It was among the North American plants introduced abroad in the early Colonial days, and a seventeenth-century Bishop of London had it in his garden at Fulham for the sake of the crimson glory of its autumnal foliage.

Not so many years ago, according to William Robinson, an unsuspecting nurseryman advertised *Rhus radicans* under a new name, *Ampelopsis Hoggi*, and the dreadful plant got a new lease of life in English gardens, putting many a poor gardener to bed with a horrid affliction unwittingly acquired and not understood. The fact that some skins are ordinarily insensitive to its action naturally added a touch of mystery to such cases. The enthusiasm of a British garden amateur is hard to quench, and I find so respectable an authority as Mr. W. J. Bean in his *Trees and Shrubs Hardy in the British Isles* including our treacherous Rhus in his list because of the beauty of its foliage in the late year, and with only a mild caution to be careful when pruning or making cuttings for propagation. Fancy *propagating* poison ivy, when all America would eradicate it from the face of the earth!

Dr. Jepson is authority for the statement that *Rhus*

diversiloba is more widely distributed in California than any other shrub. Not satisfied with that, it has spread northward well into Oregon (where the keen-eyed Douglas saw and recorded it), but fortunately for the tender of skin it cannot stand high altitudes, and above 5,000 feet one need not expect it. Nor can it endure the arduous conditions of desert life. Mr. Chesnut, in his *Plants Used by the Indians of Mendocino County*, states that he found the full-blood Indians not readily poisoned by it, but the half-breeds are often badly affected by handling it. The Pomos, the same authority states, call it *matú ya-ho*, meaning "southern fire doctor," and use it for curing warts—the wart being cut to the quick and the juice of the poison oak then applied. Formerly the fresh leaves were considered efficacious when bound about a fresh rattlesnake wound, and the basket makers found use for the stems of the plant as weaving material, and for the fresh juice as a black dye. The juice quickly turns black when exposed to the air, and is said to be an excellent substitute for indelible ink to mark linen. I leave it to a braver spirit than mine to test the truth of this statement. There are philosophers who affirm a soul of good in things evil; but in this case of poison oak it took the bees to find the best. They frequent it musically when in bloom and make an innocuous honey from the flowers. Similarly the ripe berries are eaten by the birds, particularly in winter. Only the outer pulp is digested, the seeds being ejected, so that birds may reasonably be held *particeps criminis* in the wide dispersal of the plant.[1]

A closely related species of Rhus, which may be mis-

[1] McNair: *Rhus Dermatitis*, p. 42. Univ. Chicago Press, 1923.

taken by the careless for poison oak, is its relative, *Rhus trilobata*, the squaw-bush. Like the poison oak, its leaves consist of three roundish leaflets more or less lobed, but there the resemblance ends, for they are smaller, duller and non-poisonous. Moreover, the flowers of the squaw-bush, tiny yellow affairs, appear in late winter or early spring in tight-fisted clustered spikes at the branch ends before the expanding of the leaves, to be succeeded in summer by sticky red berries, altogether different from the whitish berries of the poison oak. Again the innocuous stems and foliage of the squaw-bush are pervaded with an innocent aromatic fragrance that some people find pleasant and others unpleasant. Tastes are like that.

The plant was placed on the rolls of science by Thomas Nuttall, who collected it in the Rocky Mountains, at about the eastern limit of its range; but long before Nuttall's arrival on the Pacific slope, the Indian women had found the bush and discovered in its pliant stems an excellent basket material. Particularly has it been used for this purpose by the mission tribes of southern California, whose work is of the coiled type. The Rhus branchlets are first stripped of their bark, then split into two or three lengthy strands. These are used to wrap around slender bundles of long-stemmed grass that form the core of the coil. Nor was this the only use to which the stems were put in the Indian economy. The Luiseño women found they could bend the twigs into the shape of a fan which they used for beating seeds from plants into the gathering basket.[1]

[1]Sparkman: *Culture of the Luiseño Indians*, p. 231. University Press, Berkeley.

As for the flattish red berries, they, too, were grist to
the aboriginal mill—ground into meal in the mortars
and consumed as food, their acid flavor, I fancy, giving
a touch of spice to monotonous dishes. Also pleasantly
acid are the sticky red berries of *Rhus integrifolia*, the
miscalled mahogany, a low shrub with leathery dark
green leaves, first collected by Nuttall.

It flourishes on or near the seacoast from Santa
Barbara to Magdalena Bay in Lower California. On
seaward-fronting bluffs it often makes dense mats,
neatly pruned and trimmed to flatness by the trade
winds; farther inland, on foothill and low mountain
slopes, it may rise to a height of twelve or fifteen feet,
a sturdy little tree, stocky of trunk and wide of branch,
forming groves, which ranchers have found useful as a
source of posts, tortuous but lasting, on which to string
barbed wire.

The hard red heartwood is responsible for the popular
term "mahogany." Vacationists and mountain ramblers
more often call it lemonade-berry. The acid, gum-
coated berries, stirred in water, make an excellent
imitation of unsweetened lemonade, and equally refreshing to a parched palate—a trick adopted, perhaps,
from the Mexicans, who have long known their value
in making *limonada*. Dr. Bryant, in a paper on the
"Habits and Food of the Roadrunner of California,"[1]
tells us that the seeds of the lemonade-berry are a
favorite food of this bird during the winter, when the
comparative scarcity of lizards and insects dooms him
to partial vegetarianism.

Farther inland, *Rhus integrifolia* is replaced by the
similar appearing *R. ovata*, with rather larger glossy

[1]*Univ. Calif. Pub. Zoology*, xvii.

leaves, leathery and smooth, and berries that have a touch of sugar in their acid coating. Both these species are indifferently called lemonade-berry, though by way of differentiation sugar-bush has been proposed for *R. ovata*. People with a taste for life's smaller offerings enjoy the sight of the fat little pinkish flowers, the buds of which are set in early autumn (for Nature is a fore-handed housekeeper and does much of her spring work in the preceding year). As winter draws to a close, the clustered spikes open timidly, a few blossoms at a time, as though distrustful of the world into which they are born.

In early summer the chaparral in southern California is brightened by the white, bee-haunted flower panicles of yet another Rhus, a shrub or small tree. The leathery, dark green leaves suggested the classic laurel to Nuttall, who first described the species and so distinguished it as *R. laurina*. The foliage exhales a pleasant bitterish aroma, not unlike bitter almond. Country folk call it sumac, which, indeed, is a general name for all the non-poisonous Rhus species. Mr. Francis M. Fultz, in his excellent study of the California chaparral, entitled *The Elfin Forest*, denominates it one of the most valu-able of shrubs as a forest cover, not surpassed by any in its fire-resisting character, for which reason its seeds are more gathered than those of other shrubs in the south for reforesting chaparral slopes.

The four non-poisonous species of Rhus above men-tioned are finding a belated appreciation as garden subjects in their native state. Particularly is this the case with the lemonade-berry, the sumac and the sugar-bush for planting on arid slopes or the poor soil of dry neglected corners, where other plants languish or die outright. In such situations these non-exacting shrubs uncomplainingly accept their scant commons and generously repay you with a wealth of cheerful greenery the year round, asking nothing but the free largesse of their native earth and sky.

Pentstemon spectabilis

FAREWELL-TO-SPRING (*Godetia*)

(*Godetia grandiflora*)

CHAPTER XIX

*Of Gilia; Who Named It and Why; and Something
of Its Life in the Garden.*

In the latter part of the eighteenth century there was
dispatched from Spain, that more than commonly
civilized monarch Carlos Third being king, a scientific
expedition having for its object a study of the natural
resources of Peru. In charge of the botany were two
naturalists, Don Hipólito Ruiz and Don Joseph Pavón.
They spent several years (1778–1788) in Peru and Chile
in prosecution of their commission, and in 1794 the
results of their labor were published in a handsome
folio with numerous plates, entitled *Florae Peruvianae,
et Chilensis Prodromus,* in which for the first time the
world was made acquainted with the genus Gilia, today
a familiar name to every Californian interested in his
state's native flora, and to garden lovers everywhere.
Only one species was described by Ruiz and Pavón,
namely, *Gilia laciniata;* but since their day a few others
have been found in South America, and very many
more in western North America, which is now known to
be the stronghold of the genus. California is particularly
rich in Gilias, and largely through the efforts of David
Douglas several species had already become established
favorites in the gardens of Europe while California was
still a Mexican province. Few of our wild flowers, indeed,
take more naturally to the easy conditions of cultivated

society than these beautiful members of the phlox family.[1]

Best known of all, perhaps, in gardens, is *Gilia tricolor*, one of Douglas's introductions, now occurring in several cultivated varieties, surprising in color to one who knows the flower only in nature. It is a common foothill species of central and northern California. The wide-awake powder-blue flowers with brown-purple centers have gained the plant the popular name of bird's-eye. The tube of the flower is yellow, which makes three distinct colors in each blossom, a fact that explains obviously enough the specific end of the botanical name. The fashion in garden flowers is in some degree like that in clothes—after Europe has set the seal of approval on them, American gardens take them up. So with this Gilia.

The late Thomas Meehan of Philadelphia, distinguished alike as horticulturist and botanist, pronounced it an excellent plant for flowering in pots during the winter, to which end Philadelphians would sow the seed in August or September. A Californian finds it hard to picture this wilding of a thousand Western hills imprisoned in a pot in a steam-heated urban apartment and expected to bloom! It is interesting, I think, to learn further that in Nebraska, *Gilia tricolor* has escaped from

[1]Dr. Gray in his *Synoptical Flora N. A.*, 1886, listed about 80 species of Gilia indigenous to California, but Dr. Jepson, in his *Manual of the Flowering Plants of California*, 1925, recognizes only 20. This is because most present-day botanists regard Gray's *Gilia* as really including at least half a dozen distinct genera, to which as many different names are given. These, according to Jepson, are *Gilia*, 20 species; *Navarretia*, 20 species; *Hugelia*, 6 species; *Linanthus*, 26 species; *Leptodactylon*, 3 species; *Langloisia*, 4 species; *Collomia*, 6 species.

the gardens and is a vagrant by roadsides, as though it heard the call of home and answered. Only less well liked in cultivation are Douglas's *G. capitata* and its varieties. Their finely dissected, thread-like leaves and dense heads of blue or white flowers are common on valley and hill throughout much of California and northward. In a general way, they resemble the Chilean *G. laciniata.*

More spectacular is the scarlet Gilia—*G. aggregata.* A sociable plant, its bright red or pinkish blossoms, sometimes speckled with white, spread warm color in summer over acres of gravelly slopes and sandy flats in the higher mountains of California, northward to Canada and eastward to the Mississippi Basin. The fiery five-pointed flowers, arranged in an open panicle sometimes a foot in length at the top of a slender stem, are enough suggestive of a rocket's star-burst to warrant the common name skyrocket, sometimes heard.

The plant was first collected by the Lewis and Clark expedition. Dr. Frederick V. Coville, in his *Plants Used by the Klamath Indians of Oregon*, records a pretty legend which he heard from the children of that tribe, with respect to this plant. It seems that in the beginning of things, when the birds and animals lived together and understood one another's language, the wild doves drank no water, but only the nectar of this flower. So the plant came to be called *ohlsam-bonwas*, which means doves' drink-plant; and the little Klamath children, taking the hint, would gather the flowers, as our white children gather honeysuckle blossoms, and suck them for the sweet contents. In an article contributed to *The Sierra Club Bulletin* (Vol. XI), Miss E. Van E. Ferguson tells of the interest which the flower possesses for humming birds. In reaching for the nectar at the bottom of the long corolla tube, the bird bumps its forehead against the stamens which daub with yellow pollen the bird's head. A new species of hummer is said to have been once described by an incautious ornithologist on the strength of this yellow adornment, which, on wearing off, took the author's glory with it!

There is a considerable group of Gilias distinguished by leaves set opposite each other on the stem and divided to the base into exceeding narrow, almost threadlike pairs radiating from the stem in the manner of spokes about the hub of a wheel. These Gilias are now segregated by most botanists under the name *Linanthus* (the flower of the flax, which the blossoms in a general way resemble in shape). A ravishing little species of this group discovered by David Douglas, and twenty years later collected by William Lobb, who introduced it into cultivation abroad through the Veitch Nurseries of Chelsea and Exeter, is *Linanthus dianthiflorus*. In common speech it is called the fringed Gilia or fringed pink. In late winter and spring it bejewels the sands of arroyo bottoms and sunny mesas from Santa Barbara to Lower California—a tiny humble plant, quite hidden in blossom time under its own wealth of rosy fringed or sometimes white flowers. The corollas have the frayed edges of a dianthus flower and a throat of pale gold. The plant's ability to grow happily in dry situations fits it admirably for a place in the rock garden and in dryish borders. Seedsmen usually list it as *Gilia dianthoides*, or *Fenzlia dianthiflora*, the latter commemorating one E. Fenzli, a botanical writer of the last century and some time custodian of the Botanical Museum at Vienna.

In sandy washes from Santa Barbara, where Nuttall discovered it a century ago, eastward across the deserts to New Mexico, *Linanthus aureus*, the golden Gilia, flourishes, another pigmy, a few inches high. The bright yellow flowers tipping the plant's wiry branchlets splash with gold the desert's gravelly wastes, visible from long distances. Also of the desert, but frequent elsewhere, too, in sandy soil is *Linanthus dichotomus*, the night owl of the family, waking all night and sleeping most of the day. Toward evening the white blossoms, which are an inch across, rapidly unfold, exhaling a delicious perfume, and acres that were bare and blank a moment before become as by the wave of a magician's wand sheeted with the similitude of snow. With returning day, the flowers fold up and the lovely sight is gone, as completely as a film of snow is gone at the touch of the sun. The common name of the flower, evening snow, happily describes it. Miss Alice Eastwood is authority for the statement that the same blossom opens and closes on several successive days, growing larger each time. And then there is *Linanthus Parryae*, the smallest of all the Gilias—a very pigmy, an inch or two high, a desert lover, also, which like the fringed Gilia seems when in bloom all flower, so insignificant is the plant.

One spring day in 1876, Dr. C. C. Parry and J. G. Lemmon—the latter a Civil War veteran who lost his health at Andersonville and found it again in California, where he turned botanist—were flower hunting along the desert base of the San Bernardino Mountains; at the summit of Cajon Pass, they discovered this midget of a plant in abounding and vari-colored bloom, now blue, now white, and again yellow. Specimens were sent to Dr. Gray who pronounced it new to science, and at

Lemmon's suggestion, named it for Mrs. Parry. Lemmon's memory is preserved in many California plants, among them that other Lilliputian of the Gilia tribe, *Linanthus Lemmonii*, found in the pine belt of the San Jacinto Mountains and southward.

Quite as engaging as any of the foregoing, though of quite a different complexion is *Linanthus parviflorus*— the harlequin of its race. The quaint little flowers run through a remarkable range of colors—pink, yellow, purple, lilac, rose, cream and white, offering an irresistible temptation to hybridizers. A noticeable feature of the flowers is the slender corolla tube which is disproportionately elongated, to as much as an inch and a half; so that the flowers stick up from the clustered calyces and leaves like jewel-topped pins from their cushion. The plant is but six inches tall or so and makes an excellent bedding subject for gardens. Not long since, I saw a brilliant patch of it in a sunny corner of a Pasadena garden. The proud owner had the seeds from Germany, seven thousand miles away, and was quite ignorant that the same thing, except for the veneer that a European education had given, was growing wild by the roadsides on the outskirts of the town. Seedsmen, I believe, usually list it as Leptosiphon—in several varieties—as *roseus*, *aureus*, *hybridus* and so on. If you ask for it be sure they do not give you *Leptosiphon densiflorus*—a related species, much taller, with larger lilac or white flowers, most admirable, but in another way. This is a rather common wilding of coastal central California. There Douglas found it and introduced it into European gardens, where it still holds a place. Its nomenclatural vicissitudes have been numerous. Just at present it goes in the best botanical circles, I believe, under the name of *Linanthus grandiflorus*.

I find I was rather hasty just now in calling *Linanthus Parryae* the smallest of all Gilias. I had forgotten certain related desert annuals often so flat to the ground that a half inch is the measure of their height—the queer little gray leaves, notched and bristle-tipped, and the satiny starry flowers most endearing in delicate tones of lavender or pink, often exquisitely peppered with minute purple dots. Of the crowds who dash to the California deserts every spring for a sight of the sands in bloom, few ever see these humble Gilia cousins at all, but those who do see them are in love with them forever. There are four species, rather much alike, and you are to call them no longer Gilia, but Langloisia, a name bestowed, I read, in honor of "a most laborious and deserving botanist, the Reverend A. B. Langlois of St. Martinsville, Louisiana," who, however, seems to have had nothing in particular to do with his namesake. The earliest of the Langloisias discovered was the pink-flowered *L. Schottii*, brought to light on "the Colorado Desert, Sonora," by the botanists of the Mexican Boundary Survey in the 1850's, and dedicated by Dr. Torrey to Arthur Schott, assistant surveyor of the expedition, who seems to have had a lively side interest in plants, and made a number of interesting finds.

Apropos of plant names, Linnæus admonishes us in one of his essays to guard with respect those that commemorate botanists of worth; for this, says he, is the finest if not the only reward of their labors. Gilia is a name of the sort to fit well in this category. Ruiz and Pavón, who gave it, explain it in their Flora as bestowed in honor of Don Felipe Gil, who, with his companion Don Gaspar Xuarez, was at that time in Rome publishing his observations on some exotic plants that had been introduced into that capital. Our dictionaries and botanical manuals class him, doubtless on the strength of this statement, as a Spanish botanist, but this appears to be a mistake. According to Poggendorff (*Biographisch-literarisches Handwörterbuch*) and other more recent authorities, he was an Italian, born at Corneto in 1756, died at Rome in 1821, and his name was really Filippo Luigi Gilii. Moreover, his botanical doings were much overshadowed by his work as an astronomer, for he was during many years director of the Vatican Observatory and Beneficiat of the Basilica Vaticana, besides being author of numerous treatises on natural philosophy. Felipe Gil was presumably merely a case of hispanicizing an Italian name, just as Cristoforo Colombo became Cristóbal Colón.

CHAPTER XX

Of Wappatoo, Bladderwort and Yampah.

On landing we found the Indian who had left this morning, and who now invited us into a lodge of which he appeared to own a part. Here he treated us with a root, round in shape and about the size of a small Irish potato, which they call wappatoo. This is the common Arrowhead or Sagittifolia, so much cultivated by the Chinese. When roasted in the embers till it becomes soft, it has an agreeable taste and is a very good substitute for bread. After purchasing some of the root, we resumed our journey."

So reads the journal of Lewis and Clark for November 4, 1805, at which time the explorers had reached a point on the Columbia a few miles below the junction with the Willamette. They were a little astray in their botany when thinking this root was the same as the arrowhead of the Chinese, for this, while very similar, is a different species. What they found on the Columbia was *Sagittaria latifolia*, a plant with small white flowers and tuberous rootstock, common in ditches, ponds and marshes throughout most of North America. The erect leaves shaped like broad arrowheads have inspired the common English name arrowhead. During Lewis and Clark's stay on the lower Columbia this plant seems to have furnished a considerable part of their diet, and their journal contains several extended references to it.

The method of harvesting the root, as described by them, is interesting. The women, who did most of the gathering, were provided with light shallow canoes, from ten to fourteen feet long and about two feet wide, capable of holding one person and several bushels of roots. A woman would go into water breast high, pushing one of these canoes, and by means of her toes would grub the tubers loose, which, freed from the mud, would float to the surface of the water to be tossed into the canoe. The tubers were never out of season in that mild climate, and even in midwinter it was a common experience to see half-submerged women patiently toeing up wappatoo for hours at a time. Frémont, thirty-nine years afterward, crossing a great marsh of southern Oregon in December, on his way to California, found large patches of ground that had been dug up by Indian women in search of roots, "as if a farmer had been preparing the land for grain." He did not succeed in finding the plant for which they had been digging, but our present knowledge of the region makes it quite certain that it was a species of wappatoo. On the maps of today there is a stream thereabout called Chewaucan Creek, named from a word in the Klamath Indian language signifying "place where the arrowhead grows."[1]

On the Columbia the wappatoo was regarded as the most valuable of all roots, according to Lewis and Clark, and a considerable trade in it was carried on between the tribes of the interior and those of the coast, where it does not grow. The settling up of the country by the whites has reduced the ancient wappatoo preserves in many districts; particularly, I read, where the European carp has been introduced, as this fish has a genuine

[1]Coville: *Plants Used by the Klamath Indians*. Washington, 1897.

aboriginal relish for the tubers, giving the poor plant a race for its life.

In California, the arrowhead is abundant on the islands and tule beds of the lower Sacramento and San Joaquin rivers and their deltas, where the tubers have acquired the name of tule potatoes. The Chinese of the district long ago discovered them, and being familiar with the tubers of *Sagittaria sinensis* of their Asiatic home, made of this American cousin an article of diet and cultivated it in their market gardens.

On the placid bosom of still ponds and lakes and sluggish streams throughout the northern hemisphere there blooms another water plant, interesting for quite a different reason. This is *Utricularia vulgaris*, the bladderwort. On the Pacific coast it is not an abundant plant, and not in evidence at all, except in summer, when its yellow flowers flash out from the dull background of the water and attract the inquisitive rambler. Curious little flowers they are, with puffed-up throat and a basal spur, but not nearly so curious as what you find when you follow the flower stalk down to its source beneath the surface of the water. Floating there and spread out like a net are the thread-like leaves of the plant, branching from radiating stems a foot and a half or more long. If you take the floating plant—for it has no root—into your hand, you will detect attached here and there to the threads of leafage small translucent bladders, which are responsible for the name bladderwort, as well as for Utricularia, which is from the Latin *utriculus*, a little bottle. These bladderlets have a tale to tell. The plant is one with which Charles Darwin experimented when investigating the habits of insectivorous plants, and its bladders have been found to serve as traps for minute crustaceans, gnat-larvae and such small deer, from whose carcasses the plant absorbs nourishment as men do from oysters and beefsteaks.

It seems that each bladder has a mouth furnished with an inwardly opening valve or trapdoor, which allows the unsuspecting little animal, nosing about for adventures, to enter with perfect ease, when immediately the door slams behind him, and do what he can, he cannot open it. In his prison cell he swims and swims about, sometimes for days, until death closes a miserable existence. Then all that is worth while to his captor is sucked out, as in the case of the insects trapped in the Darlingtonia's pitcher or on the sundew's sticky paddles, as has been narrated in a previous chapter.

This ghoulish little plant occurs at several stations in the Yosemite region, as at Tuolumne Meadows, Little Yosemite, and Eagle Peak Meadows (according to Dr. H. M. Hall), and also at Lake Tahoe. There are several species of bladderwort, all addicted to this same practice, and if you care to learn of their anatomy to the minutest detail and just how they do business until their last secret is revealed, you cannot do better than read the chapters on Utricularia in Darwin's classic work *Insectivorous Plants.*

To return to the subject of edible roots with which this chapter started out. In Frémont's journal of his exploring expedition to Oregon and California in 1843–44, he tells a pleasant story of an Indian woman of the Snake nation, whom he found at St. Vrain's fort on the upper waters of the Platte River, in the country of the Arapaho. She was the widow of a French *engagé* who had been murdered shortly before in a Fourth of July brawl, and being desirous, like Naomi of old (so the journal puts it), to return to her own people from the land of the alien, she obtained Frémont's permission to accompany the expedition to the Snake villages farther west. More fortunate than the Jewish widow, she carried with her two pretty little half-breed children, and baggage enough for five or six pack animals. The season was summer, and after a few days' travel through the mountains a halt was called one noon on the most western fork of the Laramie River, a handsome stream, wide and shallow and clear, flowing rapidly over a bed of boulders and stones. Here Frémont's interest was aroused by seeing the Snake woman set to work to dig roots in the low, timbered bottomland of the creek. The roots she gathered were of one sort, slender, finger-like tubers, a few inches long, resembling small sweet potatoes in shape and taste. It seems these roots were a favorite food of the Snake Indians, who called them *yampah*. From then on *yampah* became an item of some importance in the dietary of the Frémont party, the most agreeably flavored of the several roots that necessity forced them from time to time to eat. Like its cousin the carrot, it could be consumed raw or added to the inevitable Indian stew.

Botanically *yampah* is a species of Carum, of the parsley family, and is related closely to the Old World herb that yields the caraway seed of the pastry cooks. The ornamental umbels of *Carum Gairdneri*, resembling Queen Anne's lace, brighten summer meadows, hillside thickets and dry cañon slopes from the Rocky Mountains to the Pacific. Before Frémont the Beechey expedition had found it in the vicinity of San Francisco or Monterey. Its use for food was by no means limited to the Snake Indians, but prevailed more or less among all tribes of the region where it grew. The specific name commemorates an English physician and scientist, one Gairdner, a protégé of Sir William Hooker, whose patronage secured him the post of surgeon at Fort Vancouver in the palmy days of the fur trade. The Klamaths of the Oregon-California border eat the tuberous roots of the closely related *Carum oreganum,* which they call *eh-paw.* Still another species, *C. Kelloggii,* frequent in open meadows and foothills of northern California, with stems sometimes five feet tall, sweet and aromatic, served the Indians in a rather surprising way. The outer root fibers are hard and rigid, and when bound into little cylindrical bundles did nicely for combing the aboriginal hair in primitive times.[1]

[1]Chesnut: *Plants Used by the Indians of Mendocino County.*

CHAPTER XXI

Of Manzanita, Salal and Other Heaths, Including
Washington's State Flower.

THOUGH the true heather—the "bonnie, bonnie heather" of the poets and patriotic Scotsmen—is not native to California, popular usage has fixed the name on two small evergreen shrubs more or less usual upon Sierran heights. One, red heather, is the *Phyllodoce Breweri* of science, or, as some botanists prefer to call it, *Bryanthus Breweri*, named in honor of the geologist, Dr. William H. Brewer, principal assistant of Prof. Josiah Dwight Whitney in the geological survey of California, conducted while the Civil War was being fought out on the Atlantic seaboard. His name is also given to one of the Sierra's topmost peaks. The other so-called heather is the white-flowered *Cassiope Mertensiana*, that is, of Mertens, an old-time German botanist. Both are denizens of cold, alpine summits and ridges of the Pacific slope, often forming springy beds and tangled mats, and, though of diverse appearance, are fellow members of the distinguished family of the heaths, to which also the heather of the Old World belongs. The red heather is exclusively Californian, occurring in abundance along the crest of the Sierra Nevada northwestward to the slopes of Shasta, and also cropping out far to the south at the edge of timber line on the summit of Mount San Gorgonio, southern California's highest peak. Its rosy saucers of bloom are clustered at the ends of wiry stems, which bristle with narrow little leaves like a bottle brush—to adopt Dr. H. M. Hall's graphic figure. It is an engaging little plant, inviting you to make a cushion of its matted stems. "No Highlander in heather," John Muir writes of it, "enjoys more luxurious seat than the Sierra mountaineer in a bed of blooming bryanthus."

The white heather is of a much more extended range, leaving the red relative far behind in its travels ever northward through Oregon, Washington and British Columbia to wind-swept tundras beneath the midnight sun. It was, I take it, upon specimens collected in Alaska, when Alaska was still a Russian fur-trading outpost, that the English botanist Don, who is responsible for the name Cassiope, based his studies about a century ago. One wonders in passing why he should have gone to Grecian mythology for a name to bestow upon a flower of non-Hellenic lands. It seems it had been originally described as a species of Andromeda, and when Don, in the interest of better science, found it necessary to reclassify it and put it in a new genus, what more natural than to dedicate it to one of Andromeda's relatives, best of all, her mother, Cassiope of the myth, and so save a family break. A man of sentiment was Master Don! Cassiope's slim upright stems, sometimes a foot high but oftener less, are clad in a close-fitting coat of overlapping, scale-like leaves, from the upper chinks of which the white cups of bloom (sometimes flushed faintly with pink and in form resembling lilies-of-the-valley) swing out on thread-like stalks.

This lovely flower, of all the Sierran company, seems to have been John Muir's favorite, and its praises are

Shooting Star (*Dodecatheon Clevelandii*)

Chia (*Salvia columbariae*)

Photo by J. Smeaton Chase

DESERT HOLLY (*Artiplex hymenelytra*) DEVIL'S CLAW (*Martynia*)

sung in many a passage of his books. His record of first seeing his "hardy, adventurous Cassiope" is in characteristic Muirish style. You will find it in that rare little volume, *Letters to a Friend*, under date of October 3, 1869. Muir is in the neighborhood of Castle and Cathedral peaks on the south fork of the Tuolumne River. "I had looked long and well for Cassiope," he writes, "but in all my long excursions failed to find its dwelling places, and began to fear that we would never meet, but had presentiment of finding it today, and as I passed a rock shelf, after reaching the great, gathered heaps of everlasting snow, something seemed to whisper, 'Cassiope, Cassiope!' That name was driven into me, as Calvinists say, and looking around, behold the long-looked-for mountain child!"

Another of the Heath cousinship, and one that has played an important part in the economy of the Pacific coast Indian, is the salal, *Gaultheria shallon*, which occurs in woods near the coast from Santa Barbara County northward to British Columbia. It is a low shrub with slender racemes of white or pinkish urn-shaped flowers, opening in late spring and summer and followed by a crop of edible purplish-black berries. In California it is one of the characteristic plants of the redwood belt. First discovered by Menzies when the Vancouver expedition visited the northwest coast in 1790-odd, its real title to fame dates from a stormy December day of 1805, when the Lewis and Clark party were in winter quarters at the mouth of the Columbia River. Captain Clark, half drowned from a drenching rain, sought shelter in a Clatsop Indian hut, where for his refreshment he was presented with a bowl containing "a kind of syrup pleasant to the taste" (I

quote from the journal), "made from a species of berry
common in the country, about the size of a cherry,
called by the Indians shelwell. Of these berries a bread
is also prepared, which, being boiled with roots, forms
a soup, which was served in neat wooden trenchers."
This, with some cockles, was the repast. Elsewhere in
the journal of the explorer the name of the fruit is
written shallon.

Specimens of the plant carried home were identified
by the botanist Pursh as a new species of Gaultheria, a
genus to which the eastern wintergreen or checkerberry,
common in coniferous woods of the Atlantic coast from
Georgia to Newfoundland, belongs. Availing himself
of the aboriginal word he named the plant *Gaultheria
shallon*. Some years later Douglas found the Oregon
natives calling it salal, the name by which we now best
know it. Douglas was much impressed with the palatability of the berries, and hoped that the seeds which he
sent to England would result in the shrub's finding a
place in the fruit gardens abroad as well as in ornamental plantings. His hopes, however, so far as I have
learned, have not been realized; though the plant
continues to be grown in England, according to William
Robinson, on the rougher flanks of rock gardens, while
its vigorous habit makes it an excellent covert for game.
Douglas endeavored to send some of the ripe fruit home
in a preservative, "but," he says naïvely in his journal,
"that put up . . . was by some evil disposed person
stolen for the sake of the spirits they were in"!

Widely distributed throughout California, on seaside
dunes and mesas and far up the mountain sides, is
another famous berry-bearing heath, the manzanita,
or arctostaphylos, of which there are more than twenty

well defined species indigenous to the state. They are
mostly sturdy evergreen shrubs, occasionally attaining
the dimensions of small trees, with leathery leaves that
have an alert way of standing more or less upright, like
the listening ears of an animal—an arrangement that
retards evaporation, a needful act of conservation under
the arid conditions to which many species are exposed
during much of the year.

Manzanita limbs are of a crookedness that makes the
most unimpressionable take notice. "Zigzaggy and
about as rigid as bones," Muir says of them. The
beautiful red or chocolate-colored bark of silken smooth-
ness is very thin, and the process of growth splits and
flakes it off, exposing the new bark in shades of virgin
green, which, however, sun and weather soon tan to red.
It is this startling nakedness of trunk and limb that
excites the interest of most observers. Frémont, in his
first passage of the Sierra Nevada, came upon it on the
western descent of the mountains. "A new and singular
shrub," he writes in his journal of the day, "body and
branches had a naked appearance as if stripped of the
bark, which is very smooth and thin." The shrub has
other charms, too; its pretty mantle of multitudinous
little urn-shaped flowers, in white or pink, appearing
sometimes even in midwinter; and its bounteous crop
of little "apples" usually red. The latter are responsible
for the name manzanita (a diminutive of *manzana*, an
apple), given the shrub long ago by the Spanish Californians. Around this rosy fruit much of the history of
the plant clusters. Only a little less than the acorn has
the manzanita berry entered into the dietary of the
California Indians, particularly in the north, and in
ancient days the ripening of the crop was a time of

special jubilation and feasting. The fruit was eaten
either raw or cooked, and quantities were packed home
in carrying baskets by the women and saved for winter
consumption.

Stephen Powers, author of a classic work on the
California aborigines, has estimated that an acre of
selected manzanita bushes is capable of producing as
much solid nourishment as an acre of wheat. Let the
white enthusiast beware, however, how he gorges on
the fruit, for its mealy pulp and seediness will soon clog
the digestive system unused to it, and cause serious
trouble when indulged in beyond moderation. Indeed,
though pleasurably acid, it is so mealy that one wonders
how it could tempt any palate that remembers its
juicy cousins, the salal and the huckleberry. Regarding
another use to which the manzanita berries are put,
however, white tastes and red are in perfect accord,
that is, the making of cider. The ripe fruit is scalded
and crushed, an equal quantity of water is added, and
the mass allowed to drain into a bowl.[1] The resultant
juice is—well, try it for yourself, and see if you do not
find it excellent. Frémont, in one of his diaries, speaks
of it with approval, particularly, he adds with an epi-
curean touch, when "put to cool in the running stream."
In Mission days, when iron was scarce, the hardness of
manzanita wood seems to have recommended it as a
substitute in some ways. At any rate, pegs serving as
nails and identified as of manzanita entered into the
architecture of Mission Dolores at San Francisco. Some
of the northern California Indians utilized the wood
for making tobacco pipes, spoons and so on.

[1]Chesnut: *Plants Used by the Indians of Mendocino County,
California.*

Of all the manzanitas, the Parry manzanita (*Arctostaphylos manzanita*), so called for Dr. C. C. Parry, who made a special study of the genus for many years, may be accorded the palm for size. There once stood near St. Helena in Napa County a specimen believed to be the largest of its race. It was reported to be 35 feet in height, with a crown of about the same diameter, and a trunk girth of $11\frac{1}{2}$ feet at the base. Many years ago a woodchopper had begun to cut it down for a fuel company, when a tree-loving passer-by saved the life of the fine old aristocrat by the payment of two dollars.[1] The tree is now gone, I am told; how or why, no one seems to know, but the memory of it still lingers with the older inhabitants of the region. Certain species of manzanita make extensive fine stands on barren rocky ridges or sunny slopes, forming thickets that are all but impenetrable even to bears. These animals, by the way, are exceedingly fond of the berries, a fact that explains the word *Arctostaphylos*, which means bear grape. One species, *A. uva-ursi* (this specific term also meaning bear grape), is a prostrate shrub, occurring in California only in the northwest corner of the state, whence it creeps its way northward to Alaska and around the world's boreal regions. The bear-berry of familiar language, it also plays a part in western travelers' tales as Kinnikinnik, being one of several native plants whose leaves were used in the customary mixed "smoke" of the aborigines in old times. Lewis and Clark refer to it in their journal as *sacacommis*, a term, they tell us, employed by the Canadian traders of that time, and incomprehensible to the average reader until he is informed that "the clerks of the trading companies are

[1] *Garden and Forest*, Dec. 2, 1891.

generally very fond of smoking its leaves, which they
carry about with them in a small bag"—that is to say,
sac à commis, the clerk's bag. Comfort of another sort
resides in the pliant branches, upon a bed of which
campers sometimes spread their blankets. The foliage
of most species contains a considerable percentage of
tannin, and mountain people make of it a decoction for
the relief of Rhus-poisoning, an idea probably derived
from the Indians, who similarly made a cleansing
lotion from the leaves.

Like a glorified manzanita, growing tall and properly
straight, where the manzanita is relatively dwarfish
and crooked, is Bret Harte's "captain of the western
wood," *Arbutus Menziesii*, the *madroño* of the early
Spaniards, the madrone of the word-clipping American
later comers. As in the case of the manzanita, the bark
is an arresting feature, polished and brightly red on
branches and young trunks, scaling off in thin flakes and
quills and exposing the new bark in greenish yellow.
The leathery, shining leaves, suggesting a magnolia's,
turn to crimson in summer, and as the new foliage
appears, the old falls with the peeling bark, carpeting
the ground beneath with warm autumnal color. Another
month or two, and the crown of the tree is all glorious
with the ripening berries in rough jackets of orange and
red—a feast for wild pigeons and wild men; in fact, not
to be despised by any if there be hunger to supply the
sauce. With the passing of winter there comes the new
year's flowering, in generous panicles of small waxen-
white bells, again like manzanita, as interesting to the
bees as were the berries to the pigeons. So at whatever
season has the madroño beauty to dispense, without
money and without price.

Its first entrance into history appears to have been on November 5, 1769, when Padre Crespi, in his diary of the Portolá expedition in quest of the lost port of Monterey, makes record of having for several days been seeing "many madroños, though with smaller fruit than the Spanish." *Madroño* is the Spanish name of the classic arbute tree of southern Europe, the arbutus of the ancient poets, and in mistaking the California tree for that the pioneers were not far wrong, for the arbute tree (*Arbutus unedo*) is in fact of the same genus, though specifically distinct. (You may see this exotic today in many a California garden, very beautiful in season with its dangling fruit that imitates the strawberry in appearance.) About twenty years later, Archibald Menzies, botanizing about the forested shores of northwestern America, discovered the Pacific coast madroño anew, and carried specimens home which Pursh described in his *Flora of North America*, and made the keen-eyed Scotsman's name safe for posterity by giving it to the noble tree that he had made known to the world—*Arbutus Menziesii*. In 1826 or thereabouts, that other keen-eyed Scot, David Douglas, who re-discovered so many of Menzies's plants, came upon the madroño in Oregon, and, sending seed to England, was the means of introducing it into cultivation abroad, where it may still be seen.

The range of the madroño in nature is from near the Mexican border in southern California, northward through Oregon and Washington to British Columbia. In southern California it is very local, but from the neighborhood of Monterey northward it becomes more abundant, and reaches its finest development in the fog-drenched forest regions of Mendocino and Humboldt

counties. There, according to Dr. Jepson, a height of
125 feet in some instances is attained. The famous
"Council Madroño," probably the most massive specimen recorded, was measured by Dr. Jepson in 1902,
and was found to be 75 feet high, 99 feet through the
crown in its greatest width and with a trunk girth of
24 feet at sixteen inches above the ground. From time
immemorial until recent times, this tree had been a
meeting place for coast tribes and those of the interior,
who met beneath its patriarchal branches to discuss
intertribal perplexities and arrange treaties[1]—a sort of
aboriginal Geneva! In dry barren soil, further inland,
the madroño may be little more than a shrub, but whatever the size the hard reddish wood was prized by the
Spanish Californians for making stirrups, and by others
for the high character of the charcoal produced from it
and utilized in the manufacture of gunpowder. On the
northwest coast crooked pieces of the wood, on account
of its hardness and heaviness, used to be bound around
stones and did duty as anchors for small vessels.

Often companioning the madroño and forming at
times veritable jungles beneath the redwoods in northern California and thence on to British Columbia, is
another famous berry-bearing heath, the California
huckleberry, *Vaccinium ovatum*. Its graceful, rosy stems
sometimes seven or eight feet high, thick set with trig
little shiny evergreen leaves, could hardly have escaped
the notice of Menzies, and certainly were not overlooked
by Douglas, who delighted in the pretty shrub and sent
seeds of it to England, where it soon got into cultivation,
and continues to be cherished for its ornamental qualities. In California it has a special association with

[1]Willis Linn Jepson: *The Silva of California.*

Christmas, its cheerful branches being gathered in large quantities and sold in city markets for holiday greenery. As for the juicy black berries about the size of peas, while not in the class of the luscious blueberries of eastern bogs, both whites and Indians gather them either for consumption out of hand, or to be made into pies and jellies.

And now, to close this chapter, let me say something about that noble genus of heaths, the Rhododendron, represented in California by two beautiful species, *R. californicum*, the California rose bay, a denizen of the Coast Ranges from near San Francisco north and on to Washington (which commonwealth, by the way, adopted the fine purple blossoms as the state floral emblem), and *R. occidentale*, the western azalea, rather common throughout California. The name Rhododendron, a Greek manner of saying rose-tree, has the respectability of great age, and is found in the writings of the ancient Greeks and Romans. The word originated with the former people, and, surprising to learn, was given to the oleander, which from time immemorial graced as a wilding the lands bordering the Mediterranean. Though there are now known to be some three hundred and fifty different species of Rhododendron native to various parts of the world (the Himalayas are notably rich in species) the genus appears to have been undiscovered by plant fanciers until well along toward the time of Linnæus, who is responsible for fixing the name upon the plants for which we now employ it. On this transfer of identity hangs a little tale.

Almost every writer on Rhododendrons warns us that they are poisonous plants and assures us that honey collected by the bees from the flowers is poisonous too. Poets have found copy in this idea of a smiling flower with venom at its heart, and have built pretty figures upon it. Nevertheless, Pacific coast bee-men are by no means unanimous in damning Rhododendron honey as poisonous or even liable to cause indigestion. Now, it is well understood that the oleander does harbor within it a noxious principle dangerous to life, so it would have been quite natural, with the passage of its old name to another plant, for the bad reputation of the former owner to travel with the name. Thus the cloud under which our beautiful Rhododendrons rest in this respect may well appear to be a case of an ill inheritance, not justified—in short, a case of mistaken identity. That kindly Philadelphia naturalist of the last generation, the late Thomas Meehan, thought so, and used to put forward as evidence of the Rhododendron's innocence the fact that the celebrated Dr. Bigelow of Boston was so convinced of the plant's non-poisonousness that he once ate a leaf of it and proved his point by triumphantly continuing to live.[1] But then, *per contra*, California sheep-men will tell you it is not safe to let the flocks browse upon it. So the battle wages, and meantime, in spite of all this pother, every summer the seaward mountain sides of northwestern California are serenely transformed for a space to Hymettian slopes, a myriad of bees buzzing and tumbling among the clustered rose-pink posies of the Rhododendron thickets that there abound.

That other Rhododendron indigenous to California, *R. occidentale*, better deserves the specific name *californicum* than does the rose bay, for it is of much wider

[1] *Meehan's Monthly*, Vol. I, p. 1.

distribution in the state, extending eastward to the Sierra Nevada and southward along the mountains almost to the Mexican border. Every vacationist knows it and loves it. It haunts the banks of trouty streams, overhanging the waters like another Narcissus, and long after one is back in the grind and stress of town life one's memory returns to the lovely shrub, and the delicious fragrance of its flowers, white with a love pat of buff on each upper petal. But nobody of the commonalty thinks of it as a Rhododendron, but always as Azalea, a word lifted two centuries ago by Linnæus out of a Greek dictionary and given by him to a Lapland species, growing on dry land, for "dry" is what Azalea means. After generations of batting arguments back and forth botanists have given up the task of trying to distinguish any essential difference between Azalea and Rhododendron, and both are included now in the latter name. As far as California is concerned, however, the distinction is easy, if for no other reason than that with us Azalea is deciduous, and Rhododendron evergreen. In English gardens the California Azalea has for three quarters of a century been a choice subject especially precious for its late blooming, coming into flower in June and July, well after the great Azalea display of spring is over. This quality naturally attracted the attention of hybridizers, English and Dutch, and through crossing with showier sorts, a beautiful race of late-flowering varieties has been developed.

CHAPTER XXII

Of the Mesquite, Its Legendary Origin and Its Uses, and How It Has Traveled to Hawaii; and of Its Sister The Screw-bean.

LONG, long ago, in the days of the ancients, before the white man discovered America, Quetzalcoatl, god of the wind and rain, manifested himself in Anáhuac, so it is related, and taught the Mexican people many things for their good; for instance, to build houses of stone, to weave garments, to make pottery, and to do feather work. For this he was highly honored; but when he would have reformed their religion by abolishing the horrid feature of human sacrifice that dehumanized it, he was opposed by an organized priesthood determined to have no interference in that department. Whereupon, in his displeasure, he laid upon the land the blight of aridity, metamorphosed its cacao trees into *mizquitl*, that is, mesquite, and disappeared over the western sea to return no more. Such is the legendary origin of the mesquite-tree, or honey-mesquite, indigenous to the desert regions of California and the southwest, southward through Mexico and Central America, Chile and the Argentine—*Prosopis juliflora* of the botanists.[1]

It was not such an ill turn, after all, that changing

[1] C. A. Robelo: *Diccionario de Aztequismos*, Cuernavaca, 1904, p. 237. *Juliflora*, with flowers in catkins. There are several species native to other parts of the world the flowers of which are borne in round heads.

of some of Mexico's cacao trees into mesquites; for of
the two the mesquite has proved the more diversely
useful. A nutritious food and a pleasant beverage derived from the ripe seed vessels; medicine from the
leaves and a soothing gum from the bark; textile material from the fibrous roots; honey from the blossoms;
plows, building material and fuel from the hard, close-
grained wood—all these and more this rather homely
subject, crooked of trunk and limb, sprawling and
aggressively thorny, has contributed to the economy of
a primitive people. Once every year it inclines to the
esthetic, and indulges in a dream of beauty. In early
spring, the crabbed branches, after months of bareness,
break out into lacy leafage of tenderest green, in
make-up somewhat like the foliage of the pepper-tree,
followed soon by pendent catkins of fragrant yellowish
flowers, which attract the wild bees for miles around.

Most of those uses to which the ancient Mexicans put
the tree were until recently to be witnessed among the
desert Indians of southern California and Arizona, and
may still be, if you are so lucky as to happen upon a
rancheria remote enough from public haunt to be not
entirely Americanized. There, beside a cabin in the
shade of ancient cottonwoods, will be a section of
mesquite log hollowed out by fire, the immemorial
mortar of the desert Indians, and not far away the
picturesque granary or storage basket of rudely woven
willow withes resting on a platform raised above the
ground by four posts. Removing the cover, fat old
Dolores takes out a few handfuls of dried mesquite
pods, and seating herself before the mortar thumps,
thumps, thumps with a slender stone pestle until they
are reduced to a coarse meal, a matter of perhaps eight

or ten minutes' work, not more, for the dried pods are very brittle. With a handleless crockery cup she scoops up some and smilingly passes it to you to taste. It is sweet, cloyingly sweet, for it is quarter grape sugar, and if you care, Dolores will soak some of it for you in water and serve it to you as a drink, which you will perhaps be as well satisfied to forego, for the grinding has not been very thorough and the hard seeds have probably not been affected by it at all. To Dolores and her family that makes no difference, however. Imperturbably they swallow all, large and fine, and apparently without subsequent discomfort.

The beans ripen in midsummer, and the long slender pods, in shape like attenuated string beans, then hang in pale golden clusters from the branches, which, in good seasons, are borne to the ground by the weight of their harvest. Horses, cattle and burros eat them with avidity, and thrive on them, particularly in the pulpy state.

I spoke just now of mesquite gum. It exudes from the bark where the branches fork, clear and amber colored, and has much the character of gum arabic. Like this it makes an excellent mucilage when dissolved in cold water, as well as a soothing gargle for an irritated throat. My friend, Edward H. Davis, of Mesa Grande, California, who is a mine of Indian lore acquired at first hand, tells me that this gum is boiled and utilized as a black dye for the decoration of pottery; and further that gray-headed Indians of the Colorado Valley—Yumas, Pimas and Papagos—mix the boiled mass with mud and plaster it on their hair, which is thereby turned a jetty black, however white it may have been before.

In washes and river valleys where the supply of sub-

terranean moisture is reached at a relatively shallow
depth, the mesquite may attain a height of 35 or 40
feet, but on arid slopes or mesas, it is rarely half that,
and oftener it is of shrub proportions. These shorter,
above-ground growths are as a rule remarkable for
enormous root development, because of the need to
burrow for moisture, a depth of root as much as sixty
feet or even more being attested. In mid-desert sands
the main body, as well as the roots, is at times completely buried in the drifted grit, so that what seems
an assemblage of a hundred shrubby mesquites may be
in reality the tops of as many branches from one sub-
merged trunk, striving upwards for a place in the sun,
after repeated deluging by storm-driven sand. These
mesquite "hummocks," as they are called, make a
cheerful undulation in the desert landscape; particularly
so when embroidered, as they often are in later winter
and spring, with the trailing vines of the pink-flowered
abronia, or sand verbena, which makes a colorful
tracery upon the white sands.

Through the agency of man the mesquite has been
carried to the West Indies, Hawaii and the Philippines,
where it is now naturalized. In Hawaii it is called
algarroba (mispronounced *aljarroba*), one of the names
by which it goes in Mexico, and has taken possession
of many waste lands, transforming them into fruitful
forests and jungles. Its introduction into Hawaii was
through the medium of seeds brought to Honolulu
about 1828 by a French Catholic missionary, Père
Bachelot, SS. CC., who arrived there from South
America. At his mission in Honolulu he sowed seeds of
a number of plants, but of them all, it is said, only one
algarroba seed grew, and this became the progenitor of

the race in the islands. The original tree continued to thrive on the spot where it entered the world until a few years ago, when it became necessary to move it a short distance to make way for a new building. The shock was too much for it, and it died. The dead crown was then cut away, leaving the trunk, which was preserved on the mission grounds as a memorial. By and by, a seedling *algarroba* made its appearance on the top of this trunk, doubtless from a bird's dropping, and grew lustily. Again, building operations necessitated the moving of the old trunk a few feet farther; but the movers, after digging away the earth for the purpose, met unexpected resistance; the tree would not budge from its place. Investigation revealed that the young tree on top had insinuated a tap root straight down through the old trunk to mother earth, and anchored it there. There was nothing for it but to sever this, with the result that the young tree perished. And then followed a new surprise. One day little clouds of smoke were observed rising from the summit of the ancient trunk. A lighted cigarette stub, it seems, dropped from a balcony above, had lodged in the decaying wood and started a slow fire. This gave the father in charge an idea. He had the charred parts cleared away, creating a considerable cavity. This he filled with earth and planted in it an *algarroba* seed, which germinated and at last reports had developed into a thrifty young plant, bidding fair to repeat the remarkable feat of its predecessor.[1]

In the momentous year 1776, while our Atlantic

[1]For this account of the dead trunk and its seedlings I am indebted to Father St. John O'Sullivan, of San Juan Capistrano, who spent some time in Honolulu in the autumn of 1930.

Nopal. Prickly Pear. (*Opuntia sp.*)

Woody skeleton of
stem, with napkin
ring made from it

Habitat

CHOLLA (*Opuntia Bigelovii*)

coast forefathers were busily occupied in starting the Revolutionary War, Padre Francisco Hermenegildo Garcés, priest of the Franciscan missionary outpost of San Xavier de Tucson, was off in the California wilderness preaching the gospel among the gentiles; and in the diary which he has left us of his travels, he sets down somewhat of the plants of the regions he traversed. Among these he notes as growing on the banks of the Colorado River "willows, cottonwoods, mesquites and screws." One may wonder about the screws, unless one has been upon the Mexican border and heard the word in the Spanish form *tornillo*, applied to a shapely little tree whose branches in autumn abound in clusters of cylindrical, brown seed vessels, each spirally twisted into as perfect an imitation of a screw as you will find in nature. The tree is *Prosopis pubescens*, the screw-bean mesquite, near akin to the honey-mesquite, of which we have been talking, and which it resembles in feathery leafage and catkined flowers. Its distribution is much less wide than that of its more famous relative, being limited to our southwestern deserts and the northern part of Mexico. Thomas Coulter, the botanical discoverer of the Colorado Desert, seems to have been the first of the early collectors to notice it, and it is on the strength of his specimens that the scientific name was given. The pods are characterized by the same sweetness that has made the honey-mesquite a favorite aboriginal food, and is generally used by California and Arizona tribes. It loves the sands and gravels of sunny arroyos and dry cañon slopes and the neighborhood of desert water holes, growing leisurely, its seedling infants gathered about its skirts, until it may score a century or two before the scissors of fate cut its thread of life.

CHAPTER XXIII

Of Wild Cabbage and Mustard; and a Plant That Wears Spectacles.

ONE of the conspicuous flowers in a California spring landscape is the wild black mustard (*Brassica nigra*); so it is quite surprising to learn that it is not native to the Pacific coast, but an outlander, an immigrant from Europe by way of Mexico, and probably unknown here until after the coming of the Spaniards. Its introduction is credited to the Franciscan missionaries, who would presumably have sown it about their missions for the sake of its wholesome young leaves, to which they would have been used in Spain as a potherb. Spanish Californians still gather them under the name of *quelites* (a general term for "greens") and cook them—"fry them," says one of my informants—with beans, a delectable dish. Doubtless, too, the mustard's hot seeds were cherished by the padres for the making of condiments, plasters and such matters, for they had often to be doctors to the flesh as well as to the soul. There is a tradition that in the early days the fathers, when setting out on a journey, would fill the ample sleeves of their habits with mustard seeds, to be scattered along the way in order that the plant springing up and flowering would mark the path for future farings. To the unsentimental mind the story seems highly improbable, as well as unnecessary, to account for the wide preva-

lence of the plant nowadays, for, once started, it
would naturally have been spread by the fowls of the
air—a sufficient agency, one would think, for they are
very fond of the seeds and great frequenters of mustard
thickets.

This *Brassica nigra* is, by the way, generally accepted
as the mustard of the New Testament parable, which
became a great tree and aforetime lodged the birds of
Palestine, where, indeed, it still grows, sometimes to the
height of twelve feet or so. As for its height in our
country, unless my memory deceives me, I have seen a
ranch team, with the teamster perched high on the
elevated front seat of the wagon, drive into a California
mustard thicket and be completely swallowed up from
sight, team and man, as though they were not there,
the flowery branches closing behind and over them.
Twelve feet is not unusual for a mustard stalk to grow,
when rooted in a rich swale or bottom land, with a
stoutness in proportion; so that old people will tell
you they could safely hitch a horse to one. From Mr.
Walter Nordhoff of Santa Barbara I learn of an old-time
rancher near San José, who each morning would send
his little boy to the pasture to bring in the cows, warning
him that until the last cow was accounted for he would
get no breakfast. It was sometimes a serious business
rounding up the last cow, and to widen his view over
the landscape the lad would climb a mustard stalk. As
he was a well fed youngster between six and seven years
old, you can realize something of the strength resident
in this annual European weed when fully mature. From
the same authority I have it that Mexicans, while not
particularly addicted to the corporal punishment of

their children, nevertheless, when they do switch, switch thoroughly, and it is a mustard stick they prefer to any other for the purpose. More poetic is the rôle the mustard plays in California's perennial romance *Ramona*, a thicket of it being the locale of one of the most charming passages in the book.

Mustard on our Pacific coast is not always wild. The commercial importance of its seeds, the source not only of the familiar table mustard but also of a valuable oil, long ago led to its cultivation abroad, and later to some extent in California, particularly in the Lompoc Valley near the site of the old Mission La Purísima, where it has been cultivated for almost half a century. Moreover, there is another mustard than this and only less abundantly gilding the California countryside in spring, that is, *Brassica campestris*, the yellow field mustard. It also is of European origin and apparently of much later introduction than its black sister. Yellow mustard is reputed to be the wild parent of the rutabaga, which may be, though it does not look much like it. While the black mustard does not flower until May or early summer, *Brassica campestris* blooms before winter is done, and spreads carpets of cloth of gold over hillsides and fields as early as February. It is of noticeably lower growth than the other, with charming smooth bluish-green leaves clasping the flower stem by earlike bases, very different from the dark green wrinkled herbage of the black mustard.

And then there is the so-called tansy mustard, which is not a Brassica, but *Sisymbrium pinnatum*—an erect, aristocratic-looking plant from a few inches to two feet high, with gray lacy foliage and racemes of tiny yellow bloom. It is common on dry mountain slopes and mesas particularly of the deserts, as well as about deserted cabins and abandoned ranch lands. The beautiful little reddish seeds are among those formerly ground by the Californian aborigines into *pinole* for mush. They were often used in mixture with other sorts in the nature of a condiment to leaven up the mass. Among our Mexican population the plant is called *pamito*, and the seeds are part of the stock in trade of every *botica* or drugstore in the Mexican quarters of California towns. They are crushed for outward application in poultices, being esteemed as an astringent vulnerary; or for use inwardly as a tea for summer complaints, particularly in children.

Everybody knows watercress—mustard's popular cousin—though it takes a special education to recognize its present accepted botanical name, *Radicula nasturtium-aquatica*—save the mark! Its pretty white flowers sparkle on the bosoms of springs and sluggish streams up and down the Pacific coast, as well as eastward, and there is satisfactory evidence of its presence here having antedated the Spanish occupation. Padre Crespi, in his pleasant journal of the Portolá expedition in 1769, speaks of their having discovered *berros* (so the Spanish call watercress) by many a streamside and "eye of water" along the route, and the hot succulent stems and leaves must have proved a refreshing addition to their rough diet. In 1806 Lewis and Clark gathered it by their Oregon camps. In Arizona Coronado found it along the Gila in 1541 growing in many springs. One would think in face of such testimony that it might be accorded the distinction of being a native American, yet most botanists are loth to consider it so, obstinately setting it down in their books as "naturalized from Europe," and explaining its presence by the supposititious agency of migratory water fowl with sticky feet.

On the Mohave Desert there are found two remarkable plants of the Mustard family, popularly known as wild or squaw cabbage. Their most conspicuous feature is the swollen, hollow stalk, two or three feet high, with flowers and a few leaves clinging precariously to its bulging surface, giving one at first sight the impression of its being a monstrosity. The plants are botanically known as *Streptanthus* (or by some botanists *Caulanthus*). One is *S. crassifolius*, the fat-leaved, the other *S. inflatus*, the swollen. The former species, which is also indigenous to the Great Basin region, has been a food plant of importance to the aborigines. According to Dr. Coville, in an account of the Panamint Indians,[1] who lived on the confines of Death Valley, the leaves and young stems were cast into boiling water, and after a few minutes taken out, washed in cold water and squeezed. This operation of washing was repeated five or six times and the leaves then dried. They were then ready to be boiled like cabbage, which it is said they somewhat resemble in taste. *Streptanthus inflatus*, which is probably similarly usable, is of a much more restricted habitat, not being recorded east of California. Desert people sometimes call it desert candle. The fat yellowish stem is not unlike an old-fashioned tallow dip in appearance, and the crimson blob of undeveloped flower buds at the summit bears a fair likeness to the flame.

A charming flower of the Mustard tribe is *Dentaria*—a plant that seeks to hide from the world its participation in the family hot temper by keeping it in the

[1]*The American Anthropologist*, Vol. v (Oct., 1892).

root. There are perhaps a score of species native to the northern hemisphere. On our own Pacific coast the one most in evidence is *Dentaria integrifolia* with its variety *californica*, one of the year's very earliest blossoms, shyly peeping up from the leafy mould of rich woodlands even in January. Indeed, I have known a moist warm autumn to bring it out in late November. The white tuberous rootstocks are pleasantly pungent, and, before children were taught to respect the flowers in the station where Nature placed them, they were among childhood's special delicacies, dug up and popped in the mouth under the name of pepper-root. Perhaps if its relative the radish were not so easily raised, this little plant would be worth introduction into the kitchen garden. The flowers, borne in loose racemes, are very lovely, usually in virginal white, but sometimes faintly flushed with rose. "Milkmaids," the children sometimes call them, an echo, I fancy, from English meadows where the nearly related *Cardamine pratensis* is so called.

Beloved also of children, and men of childlike spirit, is that quaint little mustard, *Dithyrea californica*, the spectacle-pod, a gray, downy-leaved herb of the deserts and of seaside dunes, the plant of the latter situations being distinguished as variety *maritima*. From a basal tuft of thickish leaves it puts up in spring a raceme of musky-scented white flowers, each in form like a tiny cross with equal arms crispy edged. No spectacles yet; you must wait a little; they come with age. When the blossoms have withered and fallen away, the seed vessels develop, until each flower's place is taken by two small, perfectly flat roundish pods side by side, with cord-like borders, a surprising imitation of a pair of rimmed eyeglasses. The common name, spectacle-pod, was inevitable. The plant was, I believe, one of the discoveries of that pioneer botanist of the Colorado Desert, Thomas Coulter, and I hope the humor of the spectacles was not lost on him.

CHAPTER XXIV

Of Thorn Apples and Desert Thorns, with an Addendum about Wild Tobacco.

IN THE days of the ancients, so runs a Zuñi legend, when the people still dwelt in the darkness of the earth's interior, a little boy and his sister came one day by chance upon a way of egress that led to this upper world of light. Day after day they would walk delightedly in the sun, with open eyes and ears, and so they learned many things that the dwellers in darkness never so much as dreamed of; and the children, upon reaching home, would tell their parents of what they had seen and heard, until the constant talking aroused the displeasure of the Divine Authorities.

Now, one day, as the boy, whose name was Aneglakya, and his sister, whose name I have forgotten, were taking an airing in the upper world, their heads filleted about with some fragrant white flowers they had plucked, they suddenly found themselves face to face with the Twin Sons of the Sun Father. Said the Divine Ones, "How do you do?" and the children answered politely in the Zuñi fashion, "We are happy." Thereupon they went on to prattle of what they knew—how they could make people sleep and have them see ghosts, how they could make them walk about and see who had stolen things, and so on. Upon hearing this the Divine Ones decided these little folk knew altogether too much, and forthwith caused the earth to swallow them up; but as the ground closed upon them forever, behold flowers of a sudden appeared upon the spot, just such flowers as the children had worn upon their heads; and the Divine Ones gave to the plant the boy's name, Aneglakya, and so it is called in Zuñi to this day. And the plant has very many children, dwelling in many parts of the earth, and some bear blossoms fringed with yellow, some with blue, some with red, and some are pure white, the symbolic colors of the four cardinal points—yellow for north, blue for west, red for south, and white for east.[1]

Such, among the stories told by the old men of the New Mexican pueblo as they sit of winter nights about the *estufa* fire, is one concerning the origin of the coarse plant that botanists knew as *Datura meteloides*. It is by no means peculiar to the Zuñi country. You have seen it by many a California roadside, two or three feet high with forking branches, its fragrant white trumpets of bloom delicately fringed with violet, unfolding in the afternoon out of rank-smelling, weedy foliage. From California it ranges eastward to New Mexico and Texas, and south far into Old Mexico. Few Pacific coast plants, if any, have entered more importantly into the religious and therapeutic activities of the aborigines than our *Datura meteloides*, which is invested with a remarkable and deadly narcotic principle akin to atropine, the soul of the medicine belladonna. Just as belladonna dropped in our ailing eyes dilates the pupils, so does a decoction of datura leaves or seeds

[1]Matilda Coxe Stevenson: "Ethnobotany of the Zuñi Indians," in 30th Annual Report, Bureau of American Ethnology, Washington, 1915.

(particularly the latter) have that same effect. Larger doses induce hallucinations, delirium, and convulsions, in which state the subject is supposed to benefit by intercourse with the powers of the unseen world, to foresee the future and to have revealed to him the hidden secrets of the past, as, for instance, the whereabouts of lost property or vanished people. Still larger doses will result in death. The Aztecs knew it well, and to them is to be credited the name for the plant current today among the people, white and Indian, both in Mexico and California, to wit, *toloache*. The etymology of this word as given by the learned Mexican scholar, the late Cecilio A. Robelo, of Cuernavaca in his curious *Diccionario de Aztequismos*, is interesting. It is, he says, a combination of the Aztec word *toloa*, meaning to bow the head, and *tzin*, a particle that indicates reverence or esteem; as one should say, "I take off my hat to you."

One of the old Spanish chroniclers in Mexico[1] tells of the Aztec priests holding this datura in such veneration that the seeds were kept in special little hampers (*petaquillas*); candles were burnt before them; and they were consulted like oracles regarding matters beyond human knowledge. These seeds are produced in round, nodding capsules, densely covered with prickles, which form an interesting and decorative feature of the plant, and have given rise to the popular name thorn-apple, sometimes given to the species. Among the southern California Indians, as well as among the Aztecs and Zuñis, reverence for *toloache* obtained, and a decoction

[1]Fr. Jacinto de la Serna, quoted by Safford in "Daturas of the Old World and New," *Annual Report Smithsonian Institution* for 1920.

of the root was used in the ceremony inducting adoles-
cent boys into full participation in a man's rights and
duties. Miss Constance Goddard Dubois, who made an
intensive study of the native customs of these Indians
twenty-odd years ago, when there were old people still
living to tell of the ancient ways, has related that the
gathering of the root was a ceremony in itself. Before
digging it up, the medicine man would address the
plant somewhat in this wise: "I have come to take you,
but not without purpose. You were placed here for
medicine, and for medicine I want you. Be not humili-
ated, O powerful one!"[1]

Aside from these mystical uses of *toloache*, the plant
was esteemed of practical value as a remedy in several
troubles of the body. Poultices, for instance, were made
of the fresh foliage for application to bruises and swell-
ings, provided the skin was unbroken; otherwise the
poisonous juice would enter the patient's blood. Cigarettes of the dried leaves, smoked for asthma, were
esteemed beneficial provided the smoker had a sound
heart. It argues well for the good sense of the Indians
that they handled this poisonous plant for centuries
with as little harm to themselves as seems to have been
the case.

Of the same botanical family with *toloache* (that is,
the Solanum or Nightshade tribe) but of a mild and
inoffensive spirit are the desert thorns, the genus
Lycium, of several species which look much alike to
the non-botanist—homely, spiny shrubs, with stubby
fleshy leaves. They are characteristic denizens of desert
washes, mesas, and arid stony hillsides from California
eastward. You will know them in the early year by

[1]Safford, *op. cit.* p. 554.

their small pallid flowers, whitish or lavender, funnel-form, with a flaring border, numerously fringing the branches. Later on comes a showy crop of red berries, each like a minute tomato in appearance, and for this reason known among the Mexican population of our southwest as *tomatillas*. Desert Indians, before their conversion to the white man's diet, found these pigmy tomatoes, either raw or boiled, a welcome addition to their monotonous menus and dried what they failed to consume fresh. In the case of at least one species, *Lycium pallidum*, the rabbit thorn (one of Frémont's discoveries, by the way, in 1844, and indigenous from the Mohave Desert in California to New Mexico) there is a curious religious association. The Navahos, accord-ing to Dr. Washington Matthews, an army surgeon who lived in their country for many years a generation or so ago, sacrificed the berries to one of their demigods to whom it was sacred; while among the Zuñis, the shrub had the reputation of being an intercessor with the gods of the harvest, and the Zuñi priests would, upon the appearance of the berries on the bush, sprinkle it with sacred meal, and pray to it that as many as the berries on its branches, so many might the people's peaches be.[1]

People who knew the island of Santa Catalina a generation ago will remember a roundish mass of green-ery fifteen feet high, that grew in the heart of Avalon and on inspection proved to be a huge, densely branched shrub. Its local name was the banyan tree, because of the drooping limbs, which brushed the ground all around banyan fashion, though they did not strike root. The more learned, however, scouted the idea of its being a

[1]Matilda Coxe Stevenson, *op. cit.*, p. 94.

banyan, and believed it to be a variety of currant, because of the crop of small red berries which it annually produced. As a matter of fact it was neither banyan nor currant but *Lycium Richii*—a rare species, native to a few parts of Mexico, including Lower California, where it is called *frutilla*, that is, little fruit. The original discovery of it is attributed to one Major Rich, whose memory is preserved in the specific name, and who found it growing at La Paz, Lower California, seventy-odd years ago. The famous Avalon specimen ended its career in 1908, when it was cut down to clear space for a building. Before that, however, specimens had been secured by various botanists, including a root cutting from which a successor to the fine old patriarch has developed, to a height of about twelve feet, in spite of the handicap of a poor location.[1] Under the name of Catalina box-thorn the species has been introduced into cultivation by Theodore Payne, its bright green foliage and cheery red berries making it a desirable subject for a bank cover or a hedge, especially near the sea.

Apropos of plants of mystical import to the Indians, there is the wild tobacco—another member of the Nightshade family and near relative of *toloache* and the Lyciums of which we have been chatting. To the aboriginals throughout America, tobacco, of which there are half a hundred species or more, was considered a sacred plant, and the smoking of it was a solemn ceremony, a sacrifice to the powers that rule life, offered to invoke divine aid or avert divine displeasure. Even today, when the white race has reduced the practice of smoking to a self-indulgence for white and red alike, the orthodox Indian continues to burn tobacco in his

[1]Millspaugh and Nuttall: *Flora of Santa Catalina Island.*

religious rites, but it must be the leaves of the wild species, not the commercial article bought at the trader's.

On our Pacific coast five or six species are indigenous, and some of them the Indians are known to have cultivated. David Douglas tells in his Oregon journal of seeing their little tobacco plantations, which were always remote from the lodges, lest the plant be gathered before maturity. An open place in the forest was chosen, where there was dead wood lying. This would be burned, and in the bed of ashes the seed would be sown, thus producing finer plants than those growing in pure nature. In California the method of smoking was to use a straight pipe, six or eight inches long, somewhat like a modern cigarette holder, made usually of clay, but sometimes from a straight bit of tree branch, with the pith burned out.

In 1540 the Spanish explorer who first set eyes on California soil, Hernando Alarcón, found the natives on the lower Colorado River "carrying small reed tubes for making perfumery," another way of saying they smoked tobacco. Apropos of this, I think it interesting to learn, as I do from Mr. Edward H. Davis of Mesa Grande, California, that among the Yumas of that region today the practice has not entirely died out in connection with ceremonial rites. The reed used is the common *carrizo* (*Phragmites communis*), of which a section a few inches long is cut between joints and stuffed with the dried pulverized leaves of wild tobacco. The smoker reclines or tilts his head up, and the reed holder burns down with the burning tobacco. These wild tobaccos are very strong, for which reason, probably, it was customary for most Indians not to smoke them pure, but in mixture, with Kinnikinnik, or what not.

An anomaly among the tobaccos is *Nicotiana glauca*, the tree-tobacco, which is a shrub or even small tree, as much sometimes as twenty feet high. It is common in waste places, and along dry stream beds and borders, often making dense thickets. It loves, too, to adorn old walls, in whose crannies the seedlings find comfortable lodgment and flourish amazingly. Its native land is Argentina, whence seeds were sent in 1827 to the Royal Botanic Garden, Edinburgh. There the plant flowered under glass and was given the "baptism of Science" as *Nicotiana glauca* because of the glaucous stem. From the Argentine it has spread northward to Mexico and the southwestern United States. Its appearance in California dates back to the Mission period, according to S. B. Parish.[1] To the present-day Californian, who regards it as a troublesome weed, it is surprising to learn that it has had something of a career in gardens as an ornamental. Indeed, its luscious young leaves, purple fringed, are quite handsome; and looking at a buxom young shoot of it one is struck with the appositeness of the Mexican common name for it, *Buena moza*, fine girl! In age, however, the plant becomes scrawny, leggy and woody, and in spite of its panicles of golden-fingered bloom, appearing and reappearing throughout the year, it loses caste in most gardens, like a frivolous old lady putting on the air of youth. As it is perennial, however, its youth can be recalled each year by a severe pruning.

Under the name Mexican tobacco, *Nicotiana glauca* is very common nowadays on Santa Catalina Island,

[1] *The Immigrant Plants of Southern California.*

Photo by Ernest Braunton

JOSHUA TREE (*Yucca brevifolia*) Mohave Desert. Believed to be the largest specimen discovered. Recently destroyed by fire.

Reproduced, by permission, from Meehan's Monthly

CALF'S HEAD (*Darlingtonia Californica*). Flowers and bud at left; leaves at right.

Photo by L. E. Martindale

Poison Oak (*Rhus diversiloba*)

Ephedra sp. (Desert Tea)

and the story of its introduction there is interesting. Until the beginning of the present century, the shrub was all but unknown on the island. Then one day, the fishermen say, the wind brought a dense cloud of smoke across the water from a great conflagration on the mainland, where the species had long been naturalized, and two or three years afterward the high ridges of Santa Catalina as well as all cañons facing the mainland abounded with the plant.[1]

[1]Millspaugh and Nuttall, *op. cit.*, p. 220.

CHAPTER XXV

*Of the Useful Sunflower and Whence It Came;
of the Goldenrod That Blooms in the Spring, and
the Autumnal Rabbit-brush with Heart of Rubber; and Other Matters.*

IN THE latter part of the year, when wild flowers are
relatively few, the cheerful colonies of the common
sunflower brighten great areas in the lowland valleys of
coastal California northward to Oregon. Like the mustard that spreads a golden mantle on the landscapes of
spring, this sunflower, *Helianthus annuus,* is not native
to the Pacific coast, but, as Asa Gray used to say of
plant immigrants in general, "a self-invited intruder."
Authorities are not altogether agreed as to its original
home, whether it included Mexico, where it has long
been in cultivation, often among the rows of maize, or
was confined to the Great Plains region of the United
States, where it abounds from Canada to Texas and
from the Mississippi to the Rockies. In Kansas it is so
much of a feature, as everybody knows, that that state
has adopted it as her floral emblem. Botanical historians
are quite convinced that its appearance on the Pacific
slope has been comparatively recent—a part, or possibly
a forerunner, of that westward march of the pioneers
which forms one of the picturesque elements of American history. Lewis and Clark recorded its abundance

among the tall grasses clothing the bottomlands of the Mississippi's upper tributaries, and were greatly interested in the Indians' use of the seeds, themselves enjoying an occasional dish of sunflower-seed meal made doughy with marrow grease. Twenty years later, Douglas found the plant established along the Columbia and the Oregon aborigines including its seeds in their dietary. After drying and pounding, the women would make of them, he tells us, "a sort of cake, not unpleasant."

But long before Douglas's day or Lewis and Clark's, the Indians of the plains and of Canada had learned the usefulness of *Helianthus annuus*. Moreover, it would seem to have been an article of commerce with them, for Champlain early in the seventeenth century saw the Hurons cultivating it as they did corn in a part of Canada where the plant was not known to be indigenous. Their special interest in it was because of the oil in the seeds, which they expressed and used for anointing their bodies and hair. The French Franciscan missionary Sagard-Theodat, who published a history of Canada in 1636, was greatly impressed by the native cultivation and use of the sunflower. "The girls reduce the seed to flour," he tells us, "in the big mortar, then they put it to boil in a large kettle of water, and after a while the oil swims on top of the soup, which the savages gather with their own spoons into their gourd bowls; and not only is this oil good to eat, but also the pounded seed, which the savages esteem an excellent thing and which I have tasted with approval. But how is it," he continues, in wonder, "that this savage people has been able to learn how to extract an oil of which we are ignorant, except by the aid of divine providence, who gives to each the means of his maintenance?"[1]

The earliest mention of the sunflower in European literature, I am told by Dr. A. W. Hill, would seem to be in a history of flowers by the Dutch physician Dodoens, published in 1568. At that time Dodoens saw the plant growing in some European garden and figured and described it, stating that it was first introduced into Spain. Obviously it must have been had from one of her American possessions, anywhere from Mexico to Kansas, though it was generally believed to be a native of Peru (Gerarde, the English herbalist of the sixteenth century, called it the Golden Flower of Peru). A deal of romantic writing was done to associate it with the Incas and Aztecs, artists pictured dusky maidens with golden sunflowers upon their breasts serving before the Temple of the Sun, and so on. Meantime, its cultivation in gardens spread. It took kindly to society life and throve mightily, developing, as time went on, a variety of races, some purely ornamental and giants of a kind, others mainly utilitarian. In the latter class are oil, cattle- and poultry-feed, paper stock and textile fiber (from the stalks) and so on. Russia began growing it about 1840 and made famous a variety with large seeds, which are toasted and consumed as Americans consume peanuts. Teachers in Los Angeles schools will tell you of their little Russian pupils' devotion to this national luxury, which they will smuggle into class, paper bags of them in their pockets.

In Mexico our annual sunflower is known by a re-markable assortment of names, as *maíz de Texas* (Texas maize), *girasol* (turns with the sun), *mirasol* (looks at

[1]*Histoire du Canada*, by F. Gabriel Sagard-Theodat. Paris, **1636.** pp. 784–785.

the sun), besides two or three Aztec survivals. *Mirasol* and *girasol* are commonly used in California among the Spanish-speaking population, and have their equivalents in the speech of many nations. The origin of the two terms is the popular notion that the flowers always face the sun, turning with it on its daily passage from east to west. One would think it only necessary to keep an eye on the garden for a day to disprove such a theory, which scientists have never hesitated to denounce, yet oddly enough there is something in it. A number of years ago, Prof. John H. Schaffner of Ohio State University conducted a series of experiments which showed that while still in bud the floral head actually starts westward shortly after sunrise, and comes to rest at sunset, when it is facing west. Shortly after midnight it begins a gradual return eastward until it faces the sun at the latter's reappearance. After the flower has outgrown the bud stage and begins to expand, this daily nutation ceases, owing perhaps to the thickening of the stalk.[1]

Besides *Helianthus annuus* one encounters on the Pacific coast several species that are indigenous, but none have so interesting a history. *H. californicus*, a tall perennial sometimes as much as ten feet high or more, is common in some parts of the state whose name it bears, particularly in the Sacramento Valley and around San Francisco Bay. It is distinguished by smooth stems and narrowish leaves, the flowers borne in loose clusters.

The sunflower's relatives, constituting with it the great world family of the *Compositae*, are legion and of diverse aspect, but by one outstanding family trait you

[1]John H. Schaffner in *Botanical Gazette*, 25:395; 29:197.

may know them, which is this: What seems a single
flower is in fact a collection of many individual florets
gathered into a compact head and held together by an
enveloping involucre, like a posy in a cup. They are the
despair of the botanical beginner in search of their
names, since there is often a great similarity in the
flowers and identification depends largely upon the
character of the seeds, an examination of which requires
patience, discrimination and a pocket lens. Nevertheless, no artificial puzzle is more fascinating or rewarding
than the puzzle which Nature sets for us in the blossoms
of this marvelous family.

One of the most widely distributed of the tribe on the
Pacific coast is *Baeria chrysostoma*, Baeria of the golden
mouth, a charming little flower with rays and disk of
golden yellow. Every spring its sociable companies
spread like a carpet in valley and on foothill slopes from
southern California to Oregon, well deserving its common name Goldfields. To Spanish folk it is *brillo del sol*,
which is their way of saying "sunshine." In old times,
they say, this was one of several daisy-like flowers that
romantic Spanish girls would pick to pieces for an
insight into the hearts of their admirers, plucking the
golden rays one by one, murmuring the while *sí, me
quieres; no me quieres* (yes, you love me; you love me
not), the last ray revealing the state of the case.

Baeria was so named nearly a century ago by the
Russian botanists Fischer and Meyer, associated with
the Imperial Botanic Garden at St. Petersburg, in honor
of another Russian, the eminent zoölogist Karl Ernst
von Baer. The species seems to have been described by
them from plants grown in the garden from seeds sent to
St. Petersburg probably from the Russian colony that

existed for well on to thirty years at Bodega Bay near San Francisco, and from which specimens of the region's flora were from time to time sent home.

Something has been said in these discursive pages about the famous naturalist Thomas Nuttall and his accompanying a trading expedition to the Pacific coast under the leadership of Nathaniel J. Wyeth in 1834. As the party left the more familiar east behind and approached the Continental Divide, Nuttall almost daily found dozens of species new to him, and his enthusiasm was intense. He would ride far ahead of the company, clearing passages with an eager hand and "looking anxiously back," so the journal of the expedition tells us, "at the approaching party as though he feared it would come and tread his lovely prizes under foot!" An unexpected result of this devotion to Flora on Nuttall's part was to awaken in the non-botanical Wyeth a desire to do some botanizing on his own account, so that on the homeward trip, Nuttall having remained on the Pacific coast, Wyeth kept an eye out for new faces among the plants and collected a number that appealed to him. Among them was a strange sunflowerish one that was picked up in the Rocky Mountains near the sources of the Columbia, and had been overlooked on the westward journey. It was turned over with other collections to Nuttall on the latter's return east, and proved to be a new genus, which he dedicated to his old leader under the name Wyethia. Since that time about a dozen additional species of the plant have been brought to light, all of them westerners and many of them Californians. They are enough like sunflowers to be mistaken for one, so that you cannot blame people for calling them that, as often happens. The coarse stems spring from a tuft of rather erect leaves, whose edges are popularly reputed to point north and south, so if you hear the plant called compass-plant, you will understand why, though this name properly belongs to a denizen of the Middle West prairies, *Silphium laciniatum.*

The California Indians long ago had their interest awakened in Wyethias, and are said to have relished the young shoots of at least one species (*W. angustifolia*), which they ate raw as a salad, while the seeds of several were harvested, as in the case of the true sunflower, parched and ground into *pinole*. So has originated another vernacular name, Indian wheat. One more is mule-ears, from the erect basal leaves, like an animal's at attention. It is rather common in the Yosemite region.

Similarly showy are the bright yellow flowers of the balsam-root (balsamorhiza), of which half a dozen species are native to the Pacific states. The deep, thick roots are noted for the presence of a turpentiny balsam, which gives the name to the plant. One of the common-est species is *B. sagittata*, the arrow-leaved, which was one of Lewis and Clark's discoveries and is native to the mountains of central California northward to Washington and east to the Rockies. The Indians learned that when the oily, resinous rind of the root was pared away the heart was edible, a fact that was taken advantage of by the hungry white pioneers of Utah in lean years, so that the plant is called Mormon biscuit in Utah to this day. Also utilized were the seeds, which were ground for *pinole*, while the young stems were eaten as greens. Altogether a plant, we may take it, that epitomizes the fare of man in that Saturnian age sung by the poets, before he became a farmer and when he accepted his sustenance from the outstretched hand of our Mother Nature.

In damp meadows of the higher Sierra Nevada grows a stately cousin of the sunflower bearing a solitary, long-stalked flower with showy yellow rays sometimes two inches long. Its most striking feature, however, is a slender dark-purple column or cone rising from the center of the flower, making an effect that once seen you do not forget. It is the California cone-flower, *Rudbeckia californica*, which was first reported in 1867 from the mariposa grove of big trees, where that Thomas Bridges of whom something was said in a previous chapter had the satisfaction of happening on it. Even nowadays it is something of an event in the plant lover's day to find it, for Rudbeckias, while common enough east of the Rockies, are by no means so on the Pacific side of the continent, where only three species occur. One of these is *R. hirta*, the familiar black-eyed Susan of eastern meadows, which joined the march westward in comparatively recent years and appears sparingly in Sierra meadows. The showy flowers of the Rud-beckias endear them to garden folk both in America and Europe, and several varieties are cultivated.

One of the most popular flowers ever introduced into gardens is the double form of *Rudbeckia laciniata*, which everybody knows as golden glow. The wild form is common in low thickets from Canada to the Gulf. The name Rudbeckia was given the genus nearly two centuries ago by Linnæus, who dedicated it to Olaus Rudbeck, father and son—"*Olao patri et Olao filio,*" so the dedication runs—distinguished instructors at the University of Upsala. There Linnæus studied under son

Olaus, then an old man, in whose home he lived for a time and tutored two young Rudbecks.

One March day on the edge of the Colorado Desert the Professor and I were astonished to find goldenrod in full bloom beside a water ditch. There was no mistaking it—typical *Solidago californica.*

"Surely, southern California is topsy-turvy land," we said, "where the rivers flow upside down and goldenrod blooms in the spring."

As a matter of fact, however, this spring blooming of the goldenrod is not to be taken too seriously, as we have since learned, for it is a peculiarity of one rare form without other distinguishing characters, found occasionally near water. Normally, California goldenrod, like its eastern kindred, waits until autumn to do its flowering, though impatient individuals will be found enlivening the dry hills of early summer. The species is abundant throughout most of California. Not content with lowland life, it takes John Muir's advice and climbs the mountains, even to a mile or more above the sea. "Sunful goldenrod," Muir called it, and found a spiritual healing in it. "The fragrance and the color and the form and the whole spiritual expression of goldenrods," he wrote to his friend Mrs. Ezra Carr, after a long sojourn in the city, "are hopeful and strength-giving beyond any other flowers that I know. A single spike is sufficient to heal unbelief and melancholy."[1] Less spiritually minded souls have associated goldenrod with the curing of the body's ills. This is indicated by the name *solidago* itself—a making solid or drawing together—which was given because the

[1]William Frederic Badè: *Life and Letters of John Muir*, Vol. ii: 10–11.

European species had a reputation as one of the noblest of vulneraries, sovereign for the healing of wounds and ulcers. Modern medicine, I believe, has banned Solidago from the books, but the old school of Spanish Californians are not of that mind, by any means. They, by the way, call it *oreja de liebre*, that is, jack-rabbit's ear, obviously suggested by the oblong, gray, slightly fuzzy leaves of the common California variety. Doña Matilde tells me—and other *ancianas*, learned in herbs and their uses, confirm the report—that it is excellent in the treatment of sores new or old, whether on man or beast, but particularly those on horses, caused by the chafing of saddle or harness—a trouble with which Californians, being from long back confirmed horsemen, have had perpetually to deal.

"The way we did," says she, "was to cut the plant off at the ground, and be sure to cut enough, *bastante*, *sabe Vd*. Then we chopped it into pieces, stem, leaves, flowers and all, so it fit the pot; then set it to boil and boil and boil. Then, while it was cooking, we took some leaves of *oreja de liebre*, young leaves are best, and put them in the oven until they were dry and easy to crumble to powder. Then when all was ready, we washed the sore place with the liquid from the pot, and then sprinkled it well with some of the powder. It was *excelente, muy excelente*." And Doña Matilde looks as pleased as though she had cured me of a stubborn case. It renews her youth to tell of the ways *de muy antes*.

Goldenrod on the Pacific coast is rarely so abundant as to influence the scenery as it so often does in the east, but of the closely related rabbit-brush or *Chrysothamnus* (that is, golden bush) the reverse is true. In numerous forms this is one of the most familiar plants of the

Mohave Desert of California and the great intramontane basin of Nevada and Utah, where it occupies thousands of square miles of arid, gravelly plain and mesa and mountain slope, transforming them for weeks in the autumn into golden landscapes worth traveling far to see. *Chrysothamnus nauseosus*, if you must have a scientific label. It is a rather low, roundish bush, often heavy scented, with usually white or gray felted stems, meager foliage and clustered heads of yellow flowers, which produce their effect through sheer numbers, since the individual blossoms are without the showy rays that give the special glory to their cousins, the sunflowers. Bees burrow and buzz in their fragrant depths; sheep, drifting southward from their northern pastures, browse them; Indians boil them to make a yellow dye, and of the stems plant windbreaks to fend off the blasts that would devastate the young garden patches.

Another Indian practice with the plant led not many years ago to remarkable results. One Judge Davidson of Inyo County, California, saw his Paiute neighbors chewing a gum, which they told him they got very simply by masticating the inner bark of a certain desert shrub. He sent specimens of it to the University of California for identification and was told it was a variety of *Chrysothamnus nauseosus*, the rabbit-brush. An analysis showed the presence of rubber, though in too small quantities to excite more than languid interest. That was in 1904. A decade passed, and the World War broke. Before long the importance of an independent rubber supply became acute in the United States. The Paiute chewing gum was remembered, and a systematic investigation of the commercial possibilities of rabbit-brush as a rubber source was instituted and carried on by Drs. Harvey M. Hall and Thomas H. Goodspeed of the University of California. Their experiments showed the existence of a considerable percentage of high-grade rubber in twelve of the twenty-two known varieties of *Chrysothamnus nauseosus*, and revealed the possibility of the cultivation of the plant on alkaline lands being developed into an important industry.[1]

[1]Hall and Goodspeed: *A Rubber Plant Survey of Western North America*, University of California Press, 1919.

CHAPTER XXVI

Of Phacelias and Nemophilas, Wild and in the Garden; of Whispering Bells and Yerba Santa, the Holy Herb.

WITH the first French exploring expedition to circumnavigate the globe, that of Louis Antoine de Bougainville in 1766 to 1769, there went as naturalist Philibert Commerson, a noted botanist of the time and friend of Linnæus. In the course of the long voyage Commerson made extensive collections of strange plants, and among them, in the Strait of Magellan, he got one whose small bluish flowers were peculiar in being borne in coiled bunches after the manner of a heliotrope. For twenty years it proved something of a puzzle and a bone of contention among botanists, who placed it first in one genus and then another, until the famous Jussieu settled the problem very cleverly by creating a brand-new genus for it, which he called Phacelia. The word was based on the Greek for cluster and was suggested by the crowded flowers of that plant from the foot of South America. Since that first discovery more than a hundred species, besides a number of varieties, have been brought to light, all natives of the western hemisphere, and most of them of western North America. About seventy-five are indigenous to California alone, among them several forms of that original gathering of Commerson's, which is exceedingly variable.

That way of producing the flower buds in compact coils which gradually straighten out with the development of the full-blown flowers, heliotrope fashion, has naturally resulted in the term wild heliotrope being applied in common parlance to many of the species. Of the many Californians an abundant sort, with finely dissected compound leaves and tight fists of blue, violet or mauve flowers, is *Phacelia tanacetifolia*, that is, the tansy-leaved (in some localities also called Fiddleneck, suggested by the half-open flower spike with its terminal coil). It is an annual common in sunny plains and valleys and on slopes of the foothills, where its tousled mounds of blue amid the scrub are a cheerful sight. Douglas's attention was attracted to it and he introduced it into European gardens, where as well as in our own it is cherished to this day. The blossoms exhale the exquisite fragrance of clover and as surely lure the bees, so that the plant is in high favor with honey men. Indeed, in some parts of Europe and in Australia (where it has also been introduced) it is regularly sown for bee pasture.

Among the Spanish Californians *Phacelia tanacetifolia* and the closely allied species *P. distans* are called *vervenía*, and are held in high esteem as a fever remedy. A decoction of the leaves is made and a cupful administered hot at bedtime—a bitter dose, which for fractious patients may be tempered with sugar. Similar as to foliage, but with flowers of a washed-out blue, is the remarkable *P. hispida*, the caterpillar Phacelia. Never was a better name. The floral spikes bristle with long, slender hairs, and your first impulse on seeing them, half uncoiled and glistening in the sun, is to start back as from a mass of crawling, humped-up caterpillars.

So rich a genus in species as Phacelia naturally includes diverse types; so, having become acquainted only with the wild heliotrope forms, you need not be surprised to learn that the wild Canterbury bell (or California bluebell, if you prefer so to call it), whose fine, violet-purple, urn-shaped flowers are a familiar sight in spring on the mesas and hills of southern California, is also a Phacelia. Thomas Coulter discovered it a century ago and carried specimens to Europe. It was named *Whitlavia grandiflora* in honor of an Irish botanist of the time, one Francis Whitla, of whom I have been unable to learn more than that he was an ardent one; but this name, Dr. Gray, for sufficient botanical reasons, some years later changed to *Phacelia Whitlavia*. Twenty years after Coulter, William Lobb came upon it, realized its garden possibilities, and sent seeds to his employers, the Veitch Nurseries in England. So began its career as a garden darling. It seems ungracious to pick flaws in so lovely a thing, but I wish it did not shed its corollas so quickly, leaving in their place only the spindling pistils.

With more open, smaller corollas than the wild Canterbury bell, and of a velvety gentian blue, are the blossoms of *Phacelia campanularia*, confined in nature to desert ranges of southern California but sensibly content with the luxury of garden life. In England a common name, I read, is Gentianelle, and William Robinson has pronounced it the best of Phacelias, the flowers lasting a long while, and the plant making a pretty carpet in sunny places—with all of which it is not hard to agree. *Phacelia Parryi*, which resembles it, was a discovery of Dr. C. C. Parry's on the mountains east of San Diego shortly after the conclusion of the

Prickly Phlox (*Gilia Californica*) beside a mountain trail

Photo by L. L. Haskin

Yampah or Squawroot (*Carum oreganum*)

Mexican War. The saucer-shaped flowers are of a deep violet hue with a remarkable five-rayed center, the rays usually about the color of the corolla but with prominent cream or white tips. Unfortunately, the herbage is rather coarse, hairy and sticky, a disappointing accompaniment to so lovely a creation. Not so disturbing, however, as in the case of that largest flowered of all the Phacelias, *P. grandiflora*, another southern Californian, occurring in the coast country from Santa Barbara to San Diego. Its wide-awake lavender blossoms an inch and a half or more across, veined in violet or purple, are most inviting; but beware, or you will find yourself smeared, skin and clothing, with an odious gummy secretion exuded from the plant's stem and leaves, which makes a stain like iron rust.

Almost every pioneer collector on the Pacific coast had a hand in extending the world's knowledge of Phacelias, a fact testified to in the names of many species. *Phacelia Menziesii* (though this it is rather the fashion now to call *linearis*) is a beautiful violet-flowered mountaineer, which Menzies discovered and Douglas rediscovered and introduced into cultivation. *Phacelia Fremontii* is a desert species with fragrant blossoms of lavender encircling a golden throat. There are plains and hills of the Mohave that are all glorious in April with this exquisite flower, linked in name with the Pathfinder, whose hands were the first, so far as known, to gather it. And there is Douglas's Phacelia (*P. Douglasii*), a neat little plant with sky-blue flowers affecting sandy soils in western central California. It has the habit and look of that much more famous wilding, its cousin *Nemophila insignis*, or Baby-blue-eyes, which Douglas plucked at Christmas time, 1830, near Monterey, upon his first landing in California. "A lovely but humble plant," he wrote of it to a friend, "the harbinger of the California spring, which forms, as it were, a carpet of tenderest azure hue. What a relief does this charming flower afford to the eyes from the effect of the sun's reflection on the micaceous sand where it grows!"

Hardly less than the California poppy does this wild flower appeal to the hearts of Californians, and, like the poppy, it occurs throughout most of the state. Moreover, it has for a century been a favorite in gardens in parts of both Europe and America where summers are reasonably moist and cool, these conditions approximating the California rainy season. Scotland's summers and those of the coast of Maine are said to be quite ideal.

My neighbor the Professor is fond of telling of a visit he had some years ago from a German lady who wished to be shown something of the California flora in its native habitats. Driving with her into the country he was startled by her suddenly crying out, "Look, look! the dear flowers of my garden at home—*die schöne Haineblumen!*" and almost before he could stop the horses, she was out and kneeling enraptured before a bank of baby-blue-eyes.

The plant first flowered in England in August, 1833, in the gardens of the London Horticultural Society, and under cultivation has developed several varieties, in fact, could hardly have helped it, since in nature it is quite variable, the blossom running in size from a half inch in diameter to an inch and a half, and in color from light blue or even white to almost indigo, sometimes delicately veined or dotted with purple. Spanish Californians call the flower *azuleja* or *azulejita*, the little

blue one. Less common nowadays but more significant
is the name *mariana*, that is, Mary's flower. This I have
encountered only in Santa Barbara, a memory of some
of the oldest families, and obviously suggested by the
flower's exquisite blue, the Virgin's color, which is often
used with white.

Besides *insignis* (which, by the way, many botanists
now combine with *N. Menziesii* under the latter term)
there are more than a dozen species and varieties of
Nemophila indigenous to the Pacific coast, some rather
insignificant of flower. One of the showier sorts is
N. maculata, the spotted, which is hardly less of a garden
favorite than Baby-blue-eyes. Each lobe of the inch-
wide white corolla is customarily marked with a violet
or purplish blotch, from which lines of minute purple
dots lead to the center of the flower. It is a plant of the
Sierra Nevada foothills and meadows, and is familiar
to flower-loving visitors in the Yosemite National Park.
Its spots have earned it the common name calico-flower.

Another noticeable species is *Nemophila aurita*, the
eared one, a would-be vine, which stretches itself for as
much as five or six feet over neighboring plants, to which
it clings by means of hooked prickles on stem and
leaves. The stem is weak and as watery as Mrs. Gum-
midge when thinking of the old 'un, and the leaves have
a curious dilated, clasping base, like the lobes of an ear,
whence *aurita*.

Altogether an oddity in the family is this climbing
Nemophila. Its choice in nature is for moist shady banks
of the foothills and cañon sides from the Sacramento
Valley to San Diego. Mrs. Parsons-Hawver has recorded
the pretty tradition that in early times the Spanish
girls in California would trim their ball dresses with

sprays of this plant, which naturally would cling pertinaciously to flimsy material. The name Nemophila, by the way, means "grove-loving," and was given the genus by Nuttall, because he found the first of the tribe growing in the shade.

Apropos of names one of the best bits of work in that line was done by the English botanist Bentham when he gave to a delightful cousin of the Phacelias and Nemophilas the name *Emmenanthe penduliflora*. It is one of Douglas's discoveries and is found on dry, sunny slopes of the foothills and deserts of California, the Great Basin and Arizona, an upstanding little plant bearing sprays of pale yellow bell-shaped flowers on thread-like stalks, with the habit of lilies-of-the-valley. When past their prime they do not wither and fall as most blossoms do, but hold their shape, become papery and persist like everlastings; and if you are lying prone among them when a passing breeze swings the pendent corollas in a rustling chime, you will appreciate the popular name, whispering bells, that some poetic soul gave them long ago. Bentham's name is no less happy, for it means "the flower that abides and droops." Forty years or so ago an enterprising plantsman introduced it into eastern gardens under the name, California yellow or golden bells, but I think it lost something of its appeal on alien soil.

Closely related to the delicate flowers we have been talking about in this chapter, though the non-botanist would never suspect it, is the noted *yerba santa*, the "holy herb" of the Franciscan missionaries, *Eriodictyon californicum* of the botanists. The small, rather handsome bluish blossoms are produced in the same close coils as distinguish the Phacelias, straightening and lengthening with the expanding of the buds. It is a shrub of dry hillsides and mountain ridges from one end of California to the other, with dark-green, glutinous leaves of a bitterish, resinous flavor not altogether unpleasant.

In some distant past, when the California Indians had the country to themselves, it was discovered that a soothing principle was hidden in this gummy foliage, valuable in troubles of the throat and lungs, and for outward griefs as well. For internal use the leaves were made into a tea; for external application, in the case of bruises and sores, a liniment was brewed and rubbed on, or a poultice of the pounded leaves was made. From their Indian neophytes the Missionary Fathers learned of the plant and its virtues, and found solace and relief in employing it as a bitter tonic and for the coughs and catarrhs that must often have afflicted them in their chilly rooms and draughty corridors. Later white comers took to it also, and families systematically kept on hand a stock of the leaves, dry or steeped in spirits. Even the United States medical profession in time became converted to faith in it—some of them, at least—and the dried leaves have official standing as a bitter tonic and balsamic expectorant useful in the treatment of asthma and chronic bronchitis. Furthermore, the leaves have remarkable power to disguise the taste of quinine—bitter against bitter; and finally, lovers of Lady Nicotine, cut off from her ministrations, have found a tolerable substitute, I am told, in smoking or chewing this blessed herb, well called holy.

CHAPTER XXVII

Of the Lupines, Their Classic Ancestry, and Some of Their California Relatives of Diverse Aspect.

UNTIL scientists can agree among themselves as to just what constitutes a species, one cannot be expected to say how many kinds of lupines there are in the world; but whatever the number, most of them by far are plants of the Pacific slope, flourishing in the region between the Rockies and the sea. That number may be a hundred or so. Outside of these limits a few are native to Latin America and the Atlantic side of the United States, including one, *Lupinus subcarnosus* or blue-bonnets, which Texans have adopted as their state emblem. Half a dozen more are indigenous to countries bordering the Mediterranean Sea. Few of our wild flowers are so much of a feature in Pacific coast land-scapes at certain seasons as these charming members of the Pea family, which in the early year carpet hundreds of acres at a stretch, their serried stems crowned with erect spires of butterfly blossoms in blue, violet, pink, white, yellow, purple or combinations of two or more of these hues.

Showy as such displays are today after a century and a half of the white man's disturbing presence, the welcome of the lupines to the early explorers was even more hearty, and the narratives of such first comers as had any taste in floral matters often made admiring note of them. The enthusiastic Douglas, with his keen eye for garden possibilities, was as ravished by the glory of them as the Spaniards were by a gold find. He introduced a score into cultivation abroad where some of them are still seen in native simplicity or civilized into aristocratic hybrids. Frémont, in his famous march up the San Joaquin Valley in the spring of 1844, was unrestrained in his delight over the thickets of blue lupine bordering the tributaries of the river. "Occasionally three or four plants were clustered together," he writes in his journal, "forming a grand bouquet, about ninety feet in circumference and ten feet high; the whole summit covered with spikes of flowers the perfume of which is very sweet and grateful. A lover of nature can imagine with what pleasure we rode among these flowering groves." In one species or another one finds lupines in every sort of situation—in the sands and gravels of the desert as well as on rich alluvial river banks; on plain and hillside, sea beach, mountain top and forest floor; in old fields and on ranch lands, where they stubbornly defend their pristine rights against plough and cattle.

By their leaves with numerous slender divisions radiating from a common center like fingers and thumb from the palm, and by the alert upstanding racemes of pea-like blossoms—a uniform plan in virtually all species—the novice may know the lupines even more surely than the daisies, which have many copies. It is to the European species of Lupinus that we owe the name—a name dignified by more than twenty centuries of use. Marvelous, indeed, how little Time, which has seen empires rise and fall, dynasties born and perish, has affected this little word. As it slips today from our American tongues, clipped of but its final syllable, any old Roman would, I fancy, infallibly know it. Virgil speaks of the "trist lupine" and its use in the agriculture of his day; from Plautus and Horace we learn that in the drama of ancient Rome actors paid their debts upon the stage in make-believe money of lupine seeds— round and flat, simulating small coins; and Pliny tells us that nothing is more "light of digestion than white lupines if they be eaten dry." (Do you remember Marion Crawford's picture of old Rome in *Ave Roma Immortalis*, the old men sunning themselves in the market places "shelling and chewing lupines as the Romans have always done"?) And there is the legend that Plutarch lived upon lupines. The particular species referred to by these writers, it is quite well agreed (and how pleasant it is to find historians and archeologists dwelling together in unity upon any subject!), was *Lupinus albus*, still a wild plant of the Mediterranean basin and also extensively cultivated there, both for its seeds, which are consumed by beast and man, and for the value of the living plant, to be ploughed under as a green manure—a fact well understood and put in practice by the farmers of ancient Latium. The seeds are bitterish things, and people who lack a bitter tooth secure an improved palatability through soaking them first in cold salt water, or boiling them in two waters. As a member of the useful family that includes peas, beans and lentils, it is not surprising to find lupine seeds with a place in the human dietary; but it is surprising, I think, that the seeds of the abounding American species seem to have been passed by as food by the Indians, whose use of the plants growing around them was so inclusive. As a matter of fact, I find a general impression that the seeds of our native lupines are poisonous, as perhaps some of them are, especially if the bitterness is not first leached out. That something tolerable was found in the roots of certain species was testified by Douglas, who confesses to "faring scantily" in a time of extremity on these and other roots.

Somewhat like the lupine in appearance but readily distinguished by leaves that are pinnate, that is, with leaflets in pairs set opposite along a common rib feather-wise, is its cousin Astragalus, the rattle-weed or loco-weed. While far less of a spectacle in the Western landscape than the lupines, the genus Astragalus is much more numerous in species—the direful spring of many botanical battles due to the difficulty of systema-tizing them. Furthermore, unlike the lupine, which is mainly North American, Astragalus in its many species is of world-wide distribution, particularly abundant in northern Asia. In the United States it loves the breezy, sun-drenched plains and prairies of the Mid-West, rioting across the Rockies and down the Pacific slope to the sea. Their racemes of narrow, close-mouthed flowers, pale yellow, dirty white, greenish or purple, are as a rule less interesting than the clustered seed vessels, which persist long upon the plants and upon which, rather than upon the flowers, the differentiation of the species is based. These are usually, though not always, blown up like bladders, in some instances as much as two inches long and nearly as much in diameter; in other cases not a quarter that size. Some are parch-ment white, some straw color, some pearl mottled with purple, others purple mottled with white; others, again, with pale cheeks touched with a blush of rose or crim-

son. Some are smooth of surface, some downy, some
rather densely short-bearded; and one I found on a
summer's day upon a California mountain top, a pigmy
of its race, whose tufted stems close to the ground bore a
crop of tiny round pods so thickly covered with a close
white nap as to resemble pellets of wool, a plant of
Douglas's finding in the north. He named it *Astragalus
Purshii* in honor of Frederick Pursh, whose *Flora of
North America* he seems to have diligently thumbed.

Shake the dry, ripened pods of an Astragalus, and
they rattle resonantly because of the ripened seeds, a
fact that obviously explains that common name rattle-
weed, which I have mentioned. As for loco-weed, it is
of more sinister import. *Loco* in the patter of the southwest means "crazy," and stock eating these plants are
apt to develop a sort of insanity; the coat becomes di-
sheveled, the eyesight is affected and the animal staggers
stupidly about, becomes emaciated and dies lingeringly.
In the case of horses the locoed individual may recover
for a time, but is subject to recurrent fits of ungovern-
able temper and plunging. Fortunately, most animals
pass the plant by, but the eating of it once begun, a
habit is formed, akin to the case of alcohol or narcotics
with man, and this, unless checked by removing the
animal to untainted pastures, goes from bad to worse.
It is not thought that all species of Astragalus are thus
noxious; indeed, the claim has been made by some
kindly experimenters that none are, but that in certain
sorts the metal barium occurs, and that it is this, taken
up unwittingly from the soil, that does the damage.[1]

Before quitting the subject of Astragalus, let me make
amends for a slighting reference just now to its flowers.

[1]Hall: *A Yosemite Flora*, p. 146.

Some of the purple-flowered sorts are undeniably of striking aspect, and one species, at least, is of such compelling beauty as to make up for whatever plainness is the lot of its confrères, and to make it an ornament in any garden capable of growing it. This is the scarlet-flowered *Astragalus coccineus*. It is of limited occurrence on arid mountain slopes bordering the western edges of the Mohave and Colorado deserts of California. Clambering one spring day up a steep, rocky trail of the Santa Rosa range, the Professor and I came face to face with this marvelous plant in full bloom, a silvery mat of leafage upon which, like so many tongues of pentecostal flame, a score of slender fiery flowers rested. Do you smile at us for a pair of silly sentimentalists if we knelt rapt in adoration of such beauty flashed upon us from that uninhabited waste? A few Old World species of Astragalus have accommodated themselves to life in our rockeries, and if this beauty of our western world could be tamed, our gardens would be the richer.

The species was first discovered by S. B. and W. F. Parish in May, 1882, in Cushenberry Cañon, near the desert base of the San Bernardino Mountains. Of these two collectors—they were brothers—S. B. Parish calls for special mention, for he made a strong impress upon the botanical history of southern California. Of New Jersey birth, he settled in 1872 on a fruit ranch near San Bernardino, where he resided for nearly half a century. In the intervals of leisure from the demands of his orchards, he traveled in easy-going fashion by camp wagon and horses over virtually every foot of southern California's valleys, mountains and deserts, studying the plant life and bringing to light a long list of species not before known. One of the kindliest and

most generous of men, he counted among his personal
friends most of the leading botanists of his time, who
when visiting California did not fail to seek "the well
worn path that led to the door of the rose-covered
Parish cottage in the San Bernardino Valley," to quote
the words of Dr. Jepson, in a sympathetic tribute published shortly after his death.[1] For the last eight years
of his life he resided in Berkeley, his home within a
short walk of the University Herbarium and Botanical
Library which he loved to frequent. He died in 1928 at
the ripe age of ninety-one. His memory is preserved
in the names of some thirty species and varieties of
California plants, besides one genus, *Parishella*, a rare
desert annual of the Lobelia family, dedicated by Dr.
Gray to the two brothers.

Near akin to the Lupine, though none would suspect
it, is Psoralea, a genus scattered about the world from
the Cape of Good Hope to British America, a few
species indigenous to California and Oregon. Linnæus
was attracted by the black or scurfy dots sprinkling the
foliage and stems of these plants, and taking them from
the company of the clovers he created for them a new
relationship, which he called Psoralea, Linnæan Greek
for scurfy or rough. Our commonest species is *P. macro-
stachya*, the leather-root, growing in cañons and on
river banks, as well as in salt marshes throughout California. It is a coarse-looking perennial from four to
twelve feet high, bearing silky clusters of rather inconspicuous purple flowers, its presence easily detected
by the pleasant fragrance exhaled by the dark-dotted
stems and leaves. The most interesting feature of the
plant to most people, as it was to the Indians, is the

[1] *Science* for January 18, 1929, p. 63.

root and the inner bark of the stems. The latter is fine and strong, and serviceable for making a primitive sort of thread; while the root pounded and resolved into its constituent fiber makes a very good textile material, especially prized for the delightful fragrance, which persists for many months.[1] Douglas seems to have been the first to introduce this plant to the world, as also its sister species *P. physodes*, rather common in the California mountains from the Santa Monica and San Gabriel ranges northward to British Columbia. It is a little shrub a foot or two high, with dense clusters of greenish-white flowers tipped with purple, the calyces dotted with tiny cup-like glands. The aromatic leaves dried and steeped in hot water are not a bad substitute for Chinese tea, and have been enough used in that way for the plant to be called in popular speech California tea.

And speaking of aromatic plants the transition from Psoralea to Parosela is natural. This is also a member of the Pea family, and its aroma, too, springs from the presence of little dots, black or red, on stem, herbage and flower. An old-time Spaniard named Cavanilles, who began his career as a priest and finished as an accomplished botanist, originated the name which, if you are good at anagrams, you may have guessed is Psoralea with the letters juggled about a bit, thereby indicating closeness of relationship. Paroselas are widely distributed in the southwestern United States and Mexico, thence along the mountains south to the Chilean Andes. In California the genus is represented by about a dozen species and varieties, characteristic children of the deserts. With two exceptions they are shrubby subjects,

[1]Chesnut: *Plants Used by the Indians of Mendocino County.*

several of them strikingly beautiful when in bloom, their small but numerous pea-like flowers of so rich an ultramarine that you marvel at the miracle of it sprung from the pallor of the desert floor. Easily chief of them all is *Parosela spinosa*, which is frequently of the dimensions of a small tree, a wraithlike tree, haunting the sandy washes of the southern desert of California and Arizona, southward into northern Mexico. Its crown of grayish-white branches and interlacing spine-tipped twiggery, innocent of all foliage, even the minutest, might deceive you from a distance into thinking you saw smoke arising from the ground, and so it has come to be called smoke-tree. That serves well enough for eleven months out of twelve, but when June is at hand another name must be had; for a mantle of indigo-blue flowers then envelops the crown, and smoke-tree turns to indigo-bush. The blossoms as they fall spread an indigo rug about the tree's base—an added grace. After the winter rains you will be likely to see the seedlings putting up, and they will surprise you with their decent little jackets of proper leafage, only to throw them off, however, a while later and go naked like their elders.

Among the early explorers Frémont, who brought home some imperfect specimens in 1849, appears to have been the first to notice the smoke-tree. Three years later, his stanch friend George Thurber, associated with the Mexican Boundary Commission, did better, and on the strength of the latter's collections the species could be regularly described and christened. That name Thurber, by the way, we often find linked with plants of the southern desert region. For four years (1850–54) he was an industrious collector along the Mexican bor-

der and added greatly to the knowledge of its botany—
an excellent botanist and one of the best hearted of men,
according to the testimony of his contemporaries. There
are, perhaps, some still living who remember his genial
"Doctor's Talks" for the children in the *American
Agriculturist*, of which for twenty years he was the
editor.

While *Parosela spinosa* defies the usual arboreal
custom as to leaves and sheds them in infancy to live the
rest of its life in Edenic nudity, other species of the tribe
are more conforming, and modestly drape their limbs
with foliage of some sort. One is *P. Schottii*, a low-
growing, spiny shrub with racemes of deep blue flowers
and simple thread-like leaves that easily distinguish it
from *P. californica* whose leaves are compounded of five
trig little leaflets. Both of these shrubs play a conspicuous part in the spring procession of the desert flowers,
and besides their richly colored blossoms offer to the
lover of small things the enjoyment of their fat little
one- or two-seeded pods. Emory's Parosela (*P. Emoryi*,
named for that Lieutenant Emory whose expedition,
you may remember, discovered the California fan-
palm) is interesting in another way. It, too, has deep
blue flowers, but few people ever see them, since they
are smothered in hairy, orange-colored calyces. If you
pinch the small flower heads between thumb and finger
you find your skin stained yellowish brown. The Indians
in old times noticed this and were able to extract a dye
from the plants by steeping the branches in water, using
it in coloring buckskins and baskets.

For three quarters of a century Paroselas were known
as *Dalea*, a name that is still popularly given them and

commemorates an old-time English physician, Samuel Dale, who published a learned work entitled *Pharmacologia* in 1693 on the nature of drugs.[1]

Often companioning the Paroselas on the desert is their arboreal cousin the Palo Verde *Cercidium Torreyanum*. The striking feature of this little thorny yellow-flowered tree is the bark, which is smooth and green on trunk, limb and twig, at least during the earlier years of the tree's life, an uncanny sort of phenomenon to one used only to seeing bark gray or brown. No wonder the Spanish-speaking pioneers named it in their graphic way *palo verde*, green timber. In old specimens the lower trunk bark turns reddish brown, but even in such the branches retain the cheerful verdancy of youth. People will usually tell you the palo verde is leafless, and so it is for most of the year; but in the early days of spring it treats its callers to the sight of a few pretty compound leaves, soon shed. Even seed pods have usually dropped by midsummer, so that for most of its days the tree is known to the traveler as only a green reticulation against a blue sky. California desert Indians formerly made an *atole* of the seeds, pounding them in mortars, thinning the meal with water, then straining and boiling—a breakfast dish of worth. The immature seeds are consumed by the Pimas and Papagos of Arizona. When quite young the seeds are cooked whole; when half grown the seed end is bitten off and the embryo plantlet squeezed out to be eaten raw or roasted in quantity in the oven. The taste is said to be much

[1]The reasons for science's abandonment of the term *Dalea* are explained in a monograph by the late S. B. Parish, "The California Paroselas," in the *Botanical Gazette* for April, 1913, to which the curious are referred.

Mesquite Hummocks, Colorado Desert, California. Pink Sand Verbena in foreground

Camp in midst of a Mesquite Tree, Colorado Desert, California

like that of very young garden peas, to which they are, of course, nearly related.[1]

We have strayed quite away from lupines and clover, but still we are not out of the family circle; and just now, when I would close the chapter, comes an annoying, straggling shrub slily tearing at my clothes with dreadful hooked spines as though asking for publicity. Every desert traveler knows *uña de gato*, the cat's-claw, *Acacia Greggii* of the botanists. From southern California it ranges east on desert hillsides and mesas and in gravelly washes through Arizona and southern New Mexico to western Texas, and southward into Mexico, where it picked up that Spanish name, which simply means claw of cat. Nothing could be more apt, for the shape of the stout spines that abundantly and abominably arm its branches is just that of pussy's particular weapon and just as keen of point. If in my resentment at its scratching I strike the bush, I myself am stricken of spirit to see its pale, delicate leaves shrink and fold their leaflets as in pain, so sensitive are they to the touch. I fancy its only true lovers are the bees, which in the spring busily buzz and hum among the spikes of yellowish flowers.

One cannot doubt that the old *conquistadores* of the sixteenth century had their attention drawn to the irritating plant and bestowed many a round Castilian oath upon it; but its appearance in scientific society dates from about 1850, when Asa Gray found specimens of it in a bundle of plants collected in our southwest by Charles Wright. Gray gave it its specific name in honor of Josiah Gregg, now chiefly remembered by his famous

[1]Frances Bonker and Dean John James Thornber, A. M.: *Sage of the Desert*, p. 71. The Stratford Company, Boston.

book, *The Commerce of the Prairies*. Gregg was a frontiersman in the years when all the southwest was part of Mexico, a man "cradled and educated upon the Indian borders." He was a friend of that Dr. Engelmann of whom we have heard in these pages as a cactus specialist, and in his travels discovered many interesting plants until then undescribed. Among them none is more generally known than this Acacia from whose attentions Gregg and his animals must often have suffered.

CHAPTER XXVIII

Of the Ice-plant, Sand verbenas and Certain Other Flowers of the Sea Beaches; and How the Little Spanish Children Played Hide and Seek Among the Malvones.

O<small>NE</small> of the untidiest rooms in California, I sometimes think, is the Professor's den, with floor, tables and shelves piled and littered with books, pamphlets, dried plants, photographs, maps, Indian curios and what not. Of course, the place has a certain fascination; one table in particular, holding a jumble of seeds and their pods, seems infallibly to lure the curious visitor. Among these odds and ends there is usually a dry twig or two studded with brown, woody, button-like excrescences each about the size of a pea, which the Professor loves to show off, for it is not so dead as it looks. Filling a saucer with water, he immerses the specimen in it; shortly there is the stir of life; the little buttons swell and gradually expand into five-pointed stars, from every arm of which there break out and drift upon the water a number of tiny, dark specks like black pepper. They are living seeds. The twig is from a plant that is found on the California seashore—a prostrate, succulent plant with herbage clammy to the touch, thickly frosted with tiny beads of imprisoned moisture which glisten like so many particles of ice. Small daisy-like, pinkish flowers mingle with the leaves, and usually there are dried stalks of an earlier growth bearing these buttons of seed vessels. It is the ice-plant of popular speech, *Mesembryanthemum crystallinum* of science, that is, the crystalline flower-of-noon, so named because the petals expand only in the middle of the day. It is one of a very large group peculiar with very few exceptions to South Africa.

One of these exceptions is our ice-plant, whose presence in the United States, limited as it is to the California coast from Santa Barbara southward, is an interesting puzzle. It is today of more restricted range than in former years, it seems, as it is reliably stated to have once covered thousands of acres[1] extending ten miles inland; but now the plough and the real estate subdivider have all but crowded it into the sea. Of the thousands of beach visitors whose feet annually crush the juicy mats of the ice-plant in their rambles and picnicking, few regard it as anything but a nuisance, yet it is a plant of economic worth, did they but know. Its young leaves make a salad acceptable to many palates (though of an ancient and fish-like taste to mine) and, I am told, are even cultivated in some European gardens for greens and garnishing. Laid between two slices of bread they make a tasty sandwich. In California they should be gathered in winter or early spring, before the ardors of summer have withered and toughened them. As you stoop to pluck them your eyes will be brought to see the exquisite beauty of the flower bud, set like a ruby in the rosy setting of calyx and involucre.

The same plant is abundant on the Canary Islands, where a considerable business was once done in burning the foliage for the soda ash, which was shipped to Spain

[1] S. B. Parish in *Zoe*, Vol. i: 263.

for use in glass making. The Spaniards call the plant *escarchada*, that is, the frosted; while in Mexico, where also it is cultivated, the preferred word is *rocío*, the dew-plant. It is readily raised from seed, and lovers of the curious have long grown it in their gardens for the oddity of the sparkling foliage. It is an annual, living but a year and dying soon after flowering and setting seeds. These are as minute as dust and carefully preserved through the dry season in the woody, tight-shut pod. This is very sensitive to moisture, and when rain falls the seams of the pod open a crack and release some of the seeds but not all. With the return of dry weather, the crack shuts to, but reopens when moisture again falls. Thus the pods open and shut and open again as the rains come and go, always dispensing some seeds and holding back some, so that loss of an early sowing is made good by a later. A canny, long-headed little plant. The seed vessels retain their vitality and sensitiveness for years, a fact that puts our ice-plant in the class of the so-called resurrection plants, of which the Rose-of-Jericho and the Mexican bird's-nest "moss," sold in curio shops everywhere, are well known examples.

On dunes and seaward-facing cliffs from San Francisco to San Diego there grows another Mesembryanthemum, the sea-fig or beach strawberry, *M. aequilaterale*. The long, trailing stems, clothed with slender, fleshy leaves, curiously three-sided and the length of one's finger, are brightened with large, daisy-like magenta flowers, each with a myriad linear petals radiant from a lighter center. The pulpy berry that succeeds the flower passes as edible, whence the common names mentioned. In Australia, where the plant is also indigenous, I find it goes by the name pig-faces; why, I leave to personal investigation. The aboriginals down there eat the leaves after baking them, and also the raw fruit. The latter is held up, squeezed between fingers and thumb, and the juice allowed to trickle into the open mouth.

A seaside plant whose right to being classed as a native Californian has been much discussed, but whose claim to that distinction is now generally admitted, is the tree mallow, *Lavatera assurgentiflora*. It is a shrub, sometimes attaining the dimensions of a small tree, belonging to the Mallow family, with maple-like leaves, amid which shyly hiding are showy, rosy flowers, darker veined. It was first published to the world by Dr. Kellogg, who described it from a cultivated specimen in a Santa Barbara garden in the early 1850's, and originating, it was said, from seed that had been brought from Anacapa, one of the Channel Islands off Santa Barbara. Long before that, however, it had been a rather common ornamental about the Franciscan missions, and there was a tradition current among the people that it had been introduced in the early days by the padres from their old Spanish homeland, for the solace of its company in their exile. But the cold eye of Science sees no basis for the pretty sentiment; for while there are species of Lavatera represented in the flora of Europe, this particular species is not known to grow there. On the contrary, all the evidence points to its being native exclusively to the islands off the California coast, where doubtless the Franciscans first became acquainted with it in the course of their missionary labors among the aboriginal inhabitants, and introduced plants at the mainland missions.

On Santa Catalina Island it is known to have been

formerly very abundant, but after the introduction of sheep and goats to the island it was eaten out of existence; so that now the only station for it thereabout is on Bird Rock, a speck of an islet off Santa Catalina's northeastern fringe.[1]

Its vogue in the early Spanish gardens was great. From a kind octogenarian informant of Santa Barbara, I learn that the old families there always planted two or three specimens of it in front of their adobe dwellings for the sake of the pretty blooms. *Malva real*—royal mallow—they called it, but elsewhere in California, *malvón*—the great mallow—was the name given, or just *malva*. Often there would be a little thicket of them, where the children would play or, when naughty, hide away from chastisement, and where truant hens would make their nests. From the same authority I learn that the plant played an important part in the domestic *materia medica* of the old days. All parts of it are mucilaginous. The leaves were boiled down to a gummy residuum, which was considered sovereign for boils, and small plants were pulled up root and all and boiled entire as a tea, which was esteemed, after *vervenía*, the best remedy for fevers.

People who remember San Francisco of a generation ago will recall the hedges of this mallow planted as windbreaks on the seaward side of the Chinese market gardens, its maritime blood probably hardening it against the salty gales that had more or less unrestricted sweep in those days across the city's suburban spaces.

On Santa Catalina and at San Juan Capistrano I have

[1]An excellent summing up of the evidence in regard to the shrub's place of nativity will be found in an article by S. B. Parish in the botanical journal *Zoe*, Vol. i: 301.

heard this tree mallow called *malva rosa*, that is pink mallow, a name acquired from the Spanish-speaking people. Any of the vernacular names are preferable to the outrageous botanical one. Nevertheless, it must be given credit for being not really malicious—it means something. *Lavatera* preserves the memory of a pair of seventeenth-century Swiss brothers, physicians and naturalists, named Lavater, and *assurgentiflora* is "the flower that looks up," expressing the engaging habit of the blossom, which first bends down and then turns upward.

One of the famous exploring expeditions of the eighteenth century was that of the French Comte de la Pérouse to the Pacific Ocean, which perished untimely of shipwreck in the South Seas with all on board. It had touched on the California coast at Monterey in 1786, and one of the naturalists of the party, Collignon by name, collected a number of plants in the vicinity, the first botanical gathering to be made in California, so far as known. Before the catastrophe that ended La Pérouse's adventure records of the expedition as far as accomplished were dispatched to France from Kamchatka. With these were a few seeds that had been secured at Monterey and were sown in the Jardin des Plantes at Paris. They were successfully germinated, and the result was a rather robust creeping plant with sticky leaves and umbels of rose-purple flowers resembling those of a verbena. A description of it from a dried specimen preserved in an herbarium in Paris was later (in 1791, to be specific) published to the world by Lamarck, the distinguished naturalist and author of a pre-Darwinian philosophy of evolution. He recognized it as a new species of the four-o'clock family and named it *Abronia umbellata*. It was the first new plant from California to receive the distinction of a scientific name.[1] A common denizen of sandy beaches from Redondo in southern California to British Columbia, it is known to every wild-flower lover as pink sand-verbena. You may think the sand-verbena of the deserts, which resembles it both in leaf and flower and every year attracts thousands to its spring flowering near Palm Springs, is the same thing, but it is not. The latter, like Esau, is of a hairy skin, a fact combined with some other peculiarities of moment to the botanical that has caused it to be classed as a different species, *Abronia villosa*, that is, the hairy.

Similar in look and habit to these two Abronias, save that the flowers are bright yellow, is *Abronia latifolia*, the broad-leaved. It adorns the coastal sands from Santa Barbara northward, and is believed to have been first seen by Menzies. Later, Dr. Eschscholz, the companion of Chamisso, of California poppy fame, collected and named it. It may be listed among plants of economic worth, for its succulent stems and foliage make an acceptable forage for hogs and cows, according to Piper and Beattie in their *Flora of the Northwest Coast*. This yellow sand-verbena is very common on the dunes near Monterey, the prostrate, trailing stems in bloom most of the year. When gales or man's activities lay bare, as sometimes happens, the plant's root system, you will marvel at the extent of it. The deep, corpulent taproot, sometimes two inches through, develops rope-like branches yards long, which burrow about under the sand in pursuit of nutriment and moisture, as well, I fancy, as a solid foothold.

[1]W. L. Jepson: *Erythea*, Vol. i: 189.

Abronias have a place of some importance in gardens both in America and in Europe, being particularly suitable for rockeries and sandy borders. The other day I saw *Abronia umbellata* seeds listed in an English catalogue at threepence and sixpence a packet, and rather wished Collignon in the Elysian Fields might know. The seed vessels of the Abronias are remarkable creations, with broad, outstanding flaps or wings. In the case of the crimson-flowered *A. maritima*, discovered by Nuttall on the beach at San Pedro and frequent along the southern California coast as far as San Diego, the pods bunched in large, round clusters have been likened to a Medusa's head.

About the oddest of seaside plants is *Salicornia*, all stem and branches, which are round and pulpy and jointed—a sort of vegetable link-sausage in make-up. There are no leaves, no flowers in the ordinary sense of the word. The organs that do duty as blossoms peep out from the chinks of the stem, mere stamens and pistils, hardly noticeable by the unaided eye, though efficient enough in producing seeds. Some plants, like some people, are like that, you say, purely practical, careless about beauty, thinking only of material results; and yet every autumn the sober green of the Salicornia's homely stems and branches is transfigured to a vivid red or crimson, and the salt marshes where it grows are sheeted with such richness of color—the corporate beauty of a myriad individuals—as draws artists from afar to paint it.

The genus in one species or another is found in saline soil on both coasts of the New World and is also common in the Old, where, as in the case of the ice-plant, its ashes have furnished soda to the glass makers; so sometimes you hear it called glasswort. Marsh samphire, another vernacular name, is less obvious. It, too, is of foreign origin, and came about in this way: On sea cliffs and shores throughout much of Europe there grows a curious, succulent plant of the Parsley family called *Crithmum maritimum*. From its love of life on ocean-fronting cliffs, it came to be associated with St. Peter, patron of fishermen, who would naturally grow familiar with it and who conjoined St. Peter's name with it. To the Italians it was *erba de San Pietro*, to the French, *herbe de Saint Pierre;* the Englishmen adopted it as sampier, eventually perverted to samphire. Salicornia, denizen of similar situations and of somewhat similar appearance to Crithmum, acquired in time the latter's name samphire with marsh prefixed as a distinguishing badge.[1] Pickle-weed, yet another common name for Salicornia, is also a case of transference from that same Crithmum, whose stems have been used for pickles. Connoisseurs, however, regard Salicornia indifferently for this purpose. So I read.

At a few isolated stations along the southern California coast as well as on the neighboring islands, there occurs the remarkable *Coreopsis gigantea*, an erect shrub with robust trunk, three or four inches thick, and sometimes as tall as a man, though oftener half that. The summit bears a crown of branches tipped with lacy leaves and clusters of golden flowers, like small sunflowers, to which family the strange plant belongs. It would seem to have nodded salutation to Anza's colonists when in late February, 1776, they passed northward from Point Concepcion, finding "all the land thickly covered with flowers." Among them Padre Font

[1]Prior: *Popular Names of British Plants.*

speaks of one as "samphire," in full bloom with yellow blossoms like small sunflowers, and trunks rising from the ground "about half a *vara*."[1] This could hardly have been anything but *Coreopsis gigantea*.

The first botanist to collect it was that Thomas Coulter who botanized in California a century ago. It was later discovered by the cattle and goats of the American occupation, who fell enthusiastically upon its foliage and have industriously browsed it out of existence to such an extent that it is nowadays one of the rarest of plants, not often seen in nature except in such inaccessible situations as cactus-guarded hilltops or the crevices of rocky bluffs. It will, however, thrive in domestication if given a sunny spot in sandy or rocky soil and a sup of water now and then, surely not much to ask. In the Botanic Garden of the university at Berkeley it has been known to persist for as long as six years. Dr. H. M. Hall states that if removed from the ground and placed in a dry room, the plant will continue to put out leaves and flowers for several weeks, the thick, fleshy stem apparently acting as a storage reservoir.

Much better known both in nature and in gardens is this giant's sister, *Coreopsis maritima*, indigenous to the coastal sands and cliffs from Santa Barbara to Lower California and on the Channel Islands—a buxom plant with much divided, succulent leaves and cheery, lemon-yellow, daisy-like flowers in early spring. It has been introduced into English gardens under the name *Leptosyne maritima*. There, although naturally a perennial, it is treated as an annual, and blooms, I hear, in the autumn. The popular name sea dahlia has become attached to the plant in California, which is unfortunate

[1]Font's Diary of the Expedition, Bolton's translation.

since it is not a dahlia, and the preferable term sea coreopsis is not such a mouthful that it should disturb anyone.

Yet another cliff dweller of the southern California coast is the so-called chalk lettuce, *Cotyledon pulverulenta*. If some botanical friend tells you this is all wrong and you should say not Cotyledon but Dudleya, do not dispute with him. It is simply a case of disagreement among the doctors. One takes one's choice. If you prefer Dudleya you are complimenting W. R. Dudley, sometime professor of botany at Stanford University.

The plant grows in a huge rosette, a foot or more across, the broad, fleshy leaves densely powdered over with a chalky dust, which is what *pulverulenta* means. It loves to sink its roots into the wrinkled faces of seaward-facing cliffs and cañon walls within reach of ocean fogs and mists, where in time it develops a short trunk. In early summer there spring up from amid the leaves stout stalks that break out at the summit into fountains of neat, conical red flowers. Sometimes, through the cracking away of a bit of rock or slide of earth, a dislodged plant may be picked up, and if taken home and hung up by the heels, indoors or out, will live for months, even developing flowers; hence another common name, air-plant.

Inland there are found other species of Cotyledon, of less robust proportions than the chalk lettuce, the leaves often slender and finger-like. They occur as a rule in the mountains in dry surroundings, and their juicy leaves are often a boon to thirsty wayfarers; so has arisen an old-fashioned name for the tribe, the hunter's houseleek. All the species are the despair of herbarium makers, for the leaves are, in fact, tight little bags of moisture, which they part with so reluctantly that drying out is a disheartening process. Dr. Coville, who made extensive collections in California a generation ago, has stated that his specimens of this genus, more than fifteen months after collection, still bore fresh leaves, which had formed while the plant was drying.

To the browser about sea borders and salt marshes from San Francisco to Lower California, a charming little shrub is the alkali heath, *Frankenia grandifolia*. Though rarely rising higher than a foot or so, it makes at times a cushiony mound of verdure many feet across, where, as in a sky of green, a multitude of small pink flowers twinkle rosily. Nothing could be neater than the trim little leaves, each with its edges turned over like the lapels of a coat collar, and you wonder why that stately tag *grandifolia*, the great-leaved, until you learn that a species with tinier leaves in the Old World was named before this, whose leaves by comparison seemed large. Our plant was first discovered "in the sands of the port of San Francisco," by that Theodor Haenke, of whom something has already been said, a botanist of the Malaspina expedition in 1791. It is salty to the taste, and chemists will tell you it contains considerable sodium chloride, which is their way of saying salt. To the Mexicans of Lower California it is *hierba reuma*, and they regard a preparation of it as a remedy for the rheums and catarrhs that beset them. It has numerous relatives abroad, frequenters of sea beaches and saline flats. The botanical name of the genus was given in honor of an old-time Swedish botanist who wrote of his country's flora nearly a century before Linnæus, one Joh. Frankenius.

CHAPTER XXIX

Of Chia and Some Other Mints, Particularly the One upon Which San Francisco Grew.

THE PROFESSOR has a ragged old garden filled with queer shrubs and trees and odds and ends of plant life from various parts of the world—plant vagabonds, most people would call them—but which he, as a botanist, cherishes for one trait or another. In the midst is a little vine-clad arbor with a bench or two and a deal table, and here one day I found him seated before a gaudy lacquered bowl, placidly sipping something from a gourd cup. He likes unconventional tableware.

"Join me," he said, pointing to another gourd that lay on the table, "and we'll travel back together to the time of the Montezumas and the Conquistadores."

"That sounds alcoholic," I rejoined, eyeing with distrust a cloudy liquid in the bowl.

"Don't you know," he replied, "that there are other things than alcohol that stimulate the fancy?—things that leave no headaches? Be an adventurer, man, and help yourself."

Somewhat gingerly I dipped out a little. It certainly was unappetizing in appearance—of a general milky hue, with dark specks swimming and bobbing about, each exuding a gooey sort of whiskers unpleasantly suggestive of—well, insects. I blinked and gulped the draught down. When I opened my eyes the Professor was looking contentedly at me.

"Well?" he inquired.

"Why," said I, "it's good. A bit queer but—got any more?"

My gourd was filled again and I sipped it with deliberation, anxious to get the benefit of the full flavor. The little specks were pleasantly mucilaginous, and yielded under the crunching of the teeth a nutty sort of taste; a suspicion of lemon and cinnamon added piquancy, and a refreshing sweetness permeated the whole.

"And now that I've done it, what have I done? and where did you get it?" I asked.

"You've drunk *agua de chia*," said he, "and the raw material was raised in this garden; but the ancestors of the seeds that I planted grew in the floating gardens of the Aztec emperors, and, together with other products of agriculture, were legal tender for imperial taxes. That's what I meant by traveling back with me to the time of Montezuma. *Agua de chia*—that is, chia water— is one of the national soft drinks of Mexico. I suppose you never heard of Mexicans drinking anything but pulque and mescal. Bad news travels faster than good. But our southern neighbor has a domestic side, and that's where chia comes in. Mexican shops in our southwest import and deal in chia as a matter of course, and my original stock was got in Los Angeles. The imported article is often mixed with adobe dust, due, I suppose, to its being threshed out on earthen floors and imperfectly cleaned; and while Mexican palates may not mind the bitterness of adobe dust, mine does; so I sowed

SNOW PLANT   DESERT CANDLE or SQUAW
CABBAGE

Field of Wild Yellow Field Mustard near Pasadena, California

some of the seed in the garden here and got a crop of my own. Have a look at it."

I did not find the plants very impressive—rather coarse-looking herbs, mostly leaves, with some spikes of plainish small blue flowers springing from the axils and the tip of the main stalk.

"Plants," remarked the Professor oracularly—he is a bachelor and enjoys his garden as parents of children enjoy their nurseries, and will talk forever about their habits and doings—"plants have been the companions of man since the beginning of the race, serving him in a thousand ways, sharing his migrations and ministering to his needs both physical and esthetic; so it is no wonder that certain ones come to have a place in his affections as firm as the love of home. One of the first naturalists to describe chia was a Mexican scholar of something over a century ago. His name was Pablo de la Llave. While still a young man he left Mexico for Spain, where he lived till he was fifty, teaching botany and acting as director of the Botanical Garden of Madrid. One day, being in Cadiz, he was presented by a friend with a little sack of chia. It awakened a thousand tender memories of his childhood in Mexico, and he has left on record how he then and there invited to a chia fiesta such compatriots as he could gather in; of how they talked, exiles that they were, of the rural fiestas of far away and long ago, of the refreshment booths of mats and reed set up in Holy Week about the village plaza, their flower-decked counters crowded with gilded gourd bowls and ollas brimming with freshly made chia."

The Professor crumpled up a brown spike or two and a quantity of small gray seeds dropped into his palm.

Returning to the table he proceeded to initiate me into the art of chia making. It seems there is quite a little trick about it, for if you do not start right the seeds stick gummily together in unpleasant clots after the fashion of lumpy oatmeal. The secret of avoiding that is to pour the seeds into the water, not the water on the seeds; so into the bowl the Professor first emptied a couple of glasses of water. Then he picked up from the table a small wooden implement somewhat resembling a very slender potato masher, but more tapering at the lower end and marked there with vertical grooves.

"This," explained the Professor, "is what they call a *molinillo*, or little mill; and while I hold it in the water and twirl it between the palms of my hands, you will drop in the seeds little by little so that they will be evenly mixed through the water."

This rite performed with due solemnity, the Professor added two teaspoonfuls of sugar, a squeeze of lemon juice, and a sprinkling of powdered cinnamon; then, after a final twirl with the *molinillo*, he poured the mixture out into two cups.

"Of course," he observed, "the little mill for stirring is not absolutely needful. A spoon will do just as well, but if you have a sense of artistic requirements, the *molinillo*'s the thing."

But there is chia and chia. All are species of salvia, that great branch of the Mint family that supplies our gardens with a score of ornamentals, as well as the sage that seasons our sausages. The Mexican species of chia of which we have been speaking is the botanists' *Salvia hispanica*. Throughout most of California, particularly in the south, as well as across into Arizona and Nevada, another chia grows that is quite famous in its way, too.

It is a prim little plant, with curiously wrinkled foliage mostly produced at the base, and smelling none too pleasant. *Salvia columbariae*,[1] the botanists call it, and it is own cousin to the chia of Old Mexico. It, also, is blue flowered, but the blossoms are borne in interrupted, buttonlike clusters through which the stem passes, skewer fashion, to the height of about a foot or even more. In the spring and early summer they spread a blue veil over many a hillside and mesa and beside mountain trails, and when the seed vessels are ripe, a pint of the tiny seeds may be gathered in a little while by a patient collector beating the heads over a bowl. In water they exude mucilage just as the Mexican sort does, and they are similarly made use of in a beverage.

It is, however, as a food that the California chia has mainly made its mark, the seeds ground into meal having from time immemorial played an important part in the aboriginal bill of fare—an essential accompaniment of every high feast and special occasion, a gift for chieftains, and the great ones of the earth. That its use is very ancient is proved by the presence of the seeds in prehistoric Indian graves, deposited, we may suppose, to nourish the itinerant soul on its journey to the land of ultimate rest. A few of our older Indians still gather this wilding crop, but with each recurring year more and more of it goes to fatten only birds and mice.

The nutty flavor of the California chia is agreeable to almost any palate, as ramblers among the hills may test for themselves, gathering it and chewing it as they walk. The late Dr. J. T. Rothrock, botanist and surgeon

[1]This name was given it about a century ago by an English botanist, George Bentham, apparently from the resemblance of the plant to *Scabiosa columbaria*.

of the Wheeler United States Geographical Survey of 1875, is one who became an enthusiastic convert to its palatability and worth. He made it the subject of extended notice in scientific papers, from one of which I make the following quotation as of practical value still:

"The seeds of chia are collected, roasted and ground. This puts it in the condition in which I first saw it. It is used as a food by mixing it with water and enough sugar to suit the taste. It soon develops into a copious, mucilaginous mass, several times the original bulk. The taste is somewhat suggestive of linseed meal. One soon acquires a fondness for it, and eats it rather in the way of a luxury than with any reference to the fact that it is exceedingly nutritious besides. It is in great demand among the knowing ones who have a desert to cross, or who expect to encounter a scarcity of water, and, what there is, of bad quality. By preparing it so thin that it can be used as a drink, it seems to assuage thirst, to improve the taste of the water, and, in addition, to lessen the quantity of water taken. As a remedy it is invaluable, for its demulcent properties, in cases of gastro-intestinal disorders. It also holds a place among domestic remedies for the same purpose that flaxseed occasionally does with us: i. e., a grain of the seed is placed in the eye (where it gives no pain) to form a mucilage by means of which a foreign body may be removed from the organ. I have found it of great service as a poultice."[1]

Another medico of the long ago, Dr. Cephas L. Bard, of Ventura, was also an enthusiast for the California chia, and has testified that a tablespoonful of the seeds was enough to sustain an Indian on a forced march of

[1]*Botany of the Wheeler Report,* p. 48.

twenty-four hours. As late as 1894 it sold as high as $6 or $8 a pound to the Spanish Californians, who found it valuable in cases of illness, since a mush or gruel made of it could be borne on a stomach that refused stronger meat. Tedious as the harvesting of the tiny seeds may seem to an American, the patient Indian woman, by a dextrous sweep of a paddle into her gathering basket, was not long in securing a goodly quantity where the plants grew thickly.

Still another variety of chia is *Salvia carduacea*, best known as thistle sage, which is the English equivalent of its botanical name. It is one of the loveliest and most remarkable of California's winter annuals, and films with lavender large areas of the lowlands and mesas in late spring, particularly in the south. It is a more robust plant than *S. columbariae*, with white cobwebby herbage and a basal rosette of thistle-like leaves. The delicate flowers in interrupted spiny whorls are remarkable for their exquisite fringed corollas, the lower segment much larger than the others and spread like an open fan, pale blue or lavender edged with white. In the center a few bright specks of orange exquisitely mark the anthers— a rare touch, that. The seeds have much the same property as those of the common chia, and have been so used, though less generally.

Douglas and Thomas Coulter independently discovered the plant about a century ago, and twenty-odd years later Wm. Lobb, famous collector for Veitch & Sons, nurserymen of Chelsea and Exeter, attempted to introduce it into English gardens, but I think unsuccessfully, as I do not find it listed in present-day English catalogues. Perhaps it languished for the dry heat of its native plains and deserts, for in California it begins to bloom only after the rains are over and the earth is parched.

A century ago all there was of San Francisco—and that was not much—clustered, a part about the Mission, and the rest about the Presidio, three miles away. Much of the area where the great city now stands was a wilderness of sand and chaparral. Through this scrubby growth two main trails ran—one from the Mission and one from the Presidio—to a small cove on the bay side of the peninsula, where it was customary for the occasional visiting vessels in that early day to cast anchor, as the situation was better protected from the wind than the Presidio anchorage. This spot, which was not far from the Portsmouth Square of today, was known as *El Parage de Yerba Buena*—the Place of the Good Herb—because of a little creeping vine, very abundant thereabout. Its sweet, aromatic fragrance, due to a volatile oil that pervades all members of the Mint family, to which it belongs, must have reminded the first Spaniards of the garden mints of their old Mediterranean home, for that name, *yerba buena*, which they gave the California wilding, is just the Spanish for mint.

Botanists call it *Micromeria Chamissonis*, in commemoration of that Adelbert von Chamisso who, I fancy, would have discovered it in one of those country rambles which yielded him the California poppy, what time the *Rurick* lay in San Francisco Bay. It loves the half shade of thin woodlands near the coast, particularly in central California. The flowers are few and hardly noticeable, but the leaves and trailing stems have long been prized by herb doctors and thrifty country folk, for making into tea for fevers, colic and sundry digestive miseries, or for use just as a tasty beverage. The plant, which is normally a few inches long, roots at the tip, and then, again and again, until a length of a yard or more may be attained.

Also of the Mint tribe, and cherished for one reason or another in the old life of California, are two species of *Trichostema*, commonly called blue-curls, because of the long, blue, curling stamens which are a conspicuous feature of the flowers. One, *Trichostema lanceolatum*, spreads a pale blue veil on arid plains, old fields and hillsides of late summer throughout western California and northward to Oregon. Even the blind will infallibly know its presence by the peculiar, not to say villainous, odor of the sticky, ashen gray leaves, a smell that is a cross between poor vinegar and worse turpentine, so that some people call the plant vinegar-weed, others turpentine-weed, and still others camphor-weed. To this list may be added tar-weed, the applicability of which will not be disputed by any who have had clothing gummed up by the glutinous foliage. Curiously enough, vinegar-weed has in its day played the diverse rôles of bee-plant (its abounding flowers being quite honeyful) and of a fish poison. The latter use is long since forbidden by law, but according to Chesnut, certain Indian tribes of the Sacramento Valley formerly employed it so. The fresh leaves were mashed up and thrown into pools or sluggish streams, the effect being to stupefy the fish, which then floated helplessly to the surface and were brought to land by hand or basket scoop. This property is shared by several other plants indigenous to California—notably the soap-weed and the turkey-mullein—as well as by others in various parts of the world whose primitive inhabitants made use of them in a similar way.

There is a shrubby cousin of the vinegar-weed more or less abundant on hills and lower mountain slopes, especially of southern California, known locally as woolly blue-curls, because of the mat of purple wool that covers the clustered flower ends. Botanically it is *Trichostema lanatum*, which means the same thing. Its foliage dispels a pleasant fragrance, and among the domestic remedies of the Spanish Californians preparations from the leaves have long held a high place. They call the plant *romero*, or *romero del país*, that is wild rosemary. Like so many of the medicinal plants of our Hispanic population, it is accounted more or less "good for everything." I think, however, it is in especial esteem for coughs and colds. Mrs. Georgiana Parks Ballard, of San Luis Obispo County, tells me that one way of treating such maladies—and a picturesque way it was—used to be to brew a steaming hot tea of the leaves in an earthenware pitcher, then cover the mouth of the pitcher with a pancake of dough, punch a hole in the latter, and inhale the escaping vapor!

In this beneficent sisterhood of the Mint family perhaps no member is better known in the southern end of California than the white sage, one of the state's most noted bee plants. The clear light amber product of its nectarful flowers is found in every grocery store where California honey is sold. Its ample silvery-gray leaves and wand-like stems, anywhere from one to three yards high, and terminating in late spring in a slender panicle of small white blooms, are ornamental enough for the garden. Foliage and stems are noticeably gummy and turpentiny of smell, facts that have gained the plant the name of greaseweed in some quarters. While very abundant within its range, this range is limited to coastal California from Santa Barbara to northern Lower California.

To the Indians, its main attraction has been its trig little seeds, brown and shiny, which they used to gather, and to some extent still do, in baskets and grind in their mortars into a meal. Before grinding, the seeds are parched, nowadays in a frying pan over a fire, but formerly more frequently by tossing about in a basket with hot pebbles or hot coals. Stirred in water with a pinch of salt, the meal is ready to serve. The seeds taste much like chia seeds, but are not mucilaginous.

The botanical name of the plant has been a battle-ground among nomenclaturists, and I am by no means sure that this fight is over. Originally named *Audibertia polystachya* in honor of the Frenchman Audibert who cultivated and wrote of exotic plants in Provence more than a century ago, it has traveled under as many aliases as an experienced "crook"; thus *Salvia californica, Ramona polystachya, Audibertia polystachya,* and *Salvia apiana.* The last (which, as you may guess, means bee-sage) was given by Dr. Jepson, who at this writing maintains it against all comers in his *Manual of Flowering Plants of California.* That name Ramona, by the way, must not deceive you into thinking it was intended to commemorate the heroine of the famous novel so called; at any rate, the giver of it, Dr. Edward L. Greene, did not say so or indeed vouchsafe any reason for it.

CHAPTER XXX

Of Sagebrush and Greasewood, Not as Useless as Sometimes Charged.

THE words sagebrush and greasewood have become so much a part of the literature of our Far West that every newcomer into the region, though non-botanical, is interested in being shown just what sagebrush and greasewood are. As a matter of fact, both terms are rather loosely used for more than one kind of desert scrub, but of the two sagebrush is the more definite of application. Let us begin with that—*Artemisia tridentata*, the three-toothed, for the leaf tips are thrice-jagged.

In California this species, the true sagebrush, is abundant on the desert ranges of the southern part of the state, and northward along the eastern slopes of the Sierra Nevada, whence it spreads across the Great Plains region to a line drawn from Montana southward to New Mexico, where the Spanish-speaking people call it and kindred species *estafiate*, a mutilated survival from the speech of the ancient Aztecs. Nevada is proud enough of its share in the plant to have made it some years ago the state's floral emblem. On the unpeopled arid plains and foothills, where it finds its most congenial home, it makes a more or less compact, silvery-green cover, a yard or so deep, and sometimes thousands of square miles in extent, almost impassable to travel.

Every pioneer of early days had his say about the "everlasting sagebrush" with which he was forced to battle. Nevertheless, at his evening camps he found a friend in its stout shaggy trunks, which for days would be the only available fuel for his fire; and had he known as much as some Indians he might have found by chewing the leaves a relief from the gripes and flatulence that so often followed his makeshift meals. To the modern agriculturist sagebrush is an indication of good land, at least for dry farming, for the soil in which it thrives is well drained and comparatively free from alkali.[1]

Though *Artemisia tridentata* must have been encountered by Lewis and Clark in the course of their overland journey in 1804–1805, the first botanist to describe and name it was Thomas Nuttall, who followed in the trail of those explorers some thirty years later, his specimens being gathered on "the plains of the Oregon and Lewis river," probably in what is now Idaho. Were it not so hopelessly common, sagebrush would be cherished for its beauty, both because of the neat gray leaves, wedge shaped and prettily notched at their wide top, and for the graceful plumes of bloom, the tiny yellowish flower heads in drooping clusterlets stringing the upright branches; so I had quite a thrill one day to learn that a number of years ago (in 1895, I believe), the shrub was introduced into England and made something of a hit among plant amateurs. They enjoyed it both for its silvery foliage, which provided an agreeable contrast to the commonplace green of ordinary shrubs, and for the aromatic fragrance exhaled for yards around the bush in humid weather.[2] This

[1]Tidestrom: *Flora of Utah and Nevada*, p. 16.
[2]W. J. Bean: *Trees and Shrubs Hardy Outdoors in the British Isles.*

terebinthine aroma, by the way, is one of the pronounced characteristics of the bush, and clings tenaciously to the clothing of all who brush against it in
passing. Barrows records its seeds as among the foods
of the Coahuilla Indians.

Of Artemisias, as of the making of books, there is
seemingly no end; though there are conservative
botanists who would limit the world's total of species
to around two hundred. They are scattered over many
parts of the earth, particularly in the northern hemisphere, and most if not all are characterized by the
presence of a bitter aromatic principle that in one
European species at least (*Artemisia absinthium*) has
been utilized in the manufacture of a famous vermifuge,
and so acquired the popular name wormwood.

In the western United States and Mexico there are
some fifty different species, but the distinctions between
many of them are not noticeable to many but botanists.
In some cases the leaves are in threadlike divisions, and
of such is *Artemisia californica*, the California sagebrush,
common on sunny hills from the San Francisco Bay
region to Lower California. It is familiar to all country
people, who sometimes call it hillbrush, but oftener
old man. A tea brewed from its aromatic foliage has long
been a popular cure-all, but especially given for fever
and colds. It was of this plant that Aunt Ri, in *Ramona*,
made a decoction to cure the heroine's fever after the
tragic death of Alessandro. Spanish-speaking Californians call it *romerillo*—little rosemary, and its stems
make a favorite *limpiatunas*, or brush for the removal
of the irritating spicules from the fruit of the prickly
pear cactus. The Luiseño Indians of southern California

will tell you that nothing is better than the smoke of burning *romerillo* for neutralizing the effect of a spraying from an incensed skunk, a fact—if it be a fact—worth remembering against a time of need.

That odd name, old man, has a history that goes back to ancient Rome. Indigenous to southern Europe and the Mediterranean basin is a nearly related species of Artemisia (*A. abrotanum*) the leaves of which, according to Pliny, were recommended to elderly Roman gentlemen as a restorer of youthful vigor, if placed under the pillow at night. Eventually this plant was introduced into English gardens for the sake of the aromatic foliage, and because of its southern origin, I suppose, called southernwood; but evidently the story of its marvelous power of rejuvenation came with it, for the English country folk have long known it as old man. Now the California sagebrush so much resembles it, both in looks and fragrance, that its English name became attached to the California plant by immigrants of Anglo-Saxon stock. Another popular name for it is lad's-love, also a legacy from the ancient doctors, who prescribed an ointment made from the ashes of southernwood to stimulate the growth of a youth's sprouting beard.[1]

Frequent in alkaline valleys and on plains and hill slopes of the Mohave Desert northward and eastward, often in company with *Artemisia tridentata*, is the curious hop-sage—*Grayia spinosa*. After flowering, which is inconspicuous, the stout bushy stems become topheavy with huge compound clusters of seed vessels, each bony seed encased in a skintight, beruffled jacket with broad flaring wings, sometimes green but often pink or crim-

[1] R. C. A. Prior: *Popular Names of British Plants.*

son—a colorful trait that makes friends for it as a thing of cheer in the midst of gray monotony. It belongs to the homely Goosefoot or Pigweed family (Chenopodiaceae) of which the beet, the spinach and a lot of barnyard weeds are members. It seems first to have been noticed by David Douglas in the Columbia River country. The botanic name was given out of compliment to Asa Gray, who, on his first visit to Europe in 1838, speaks of the matter in one of his racy letters home. "Hooker has a curious new genus of Chenopodiaceae from the Rocky Mountains," he writes, "which he wishes to call Grayia! I am quite content with a Pigweed, and this is a very queer one." Gray was at the time still a comparative youngster, only twenty-eight, and to have any sort of plant named for him was flattering; but in view of the brilliant career that was to be his, one may be pardoned the regret that his friend Hooker had not waited for something better, for after you have had one genus named for you, you cannot have another.

And so we come naturally to the consideration of greasewood, for it is to the Pigweed family that one of the best known plants going by this name belongs, the odd *Sarcobatus vermiculatus*. It is a white-barked, intricately branched, somewhat spiny bush, sometimes four feet high or more, with narrow fleshy leaves, and bearing at many branch ends conspicuous spikes of close-packed flowers, though without a special education you would not suspect them of being flowers, for they are quite tiny, corolla-less and reduced to the bare elements, that is, stamens or pistils. It is one of the most widely dispersed of desert plants, and the bright green of its foliage, in contrast to the monotonous gray of the

neighboring saltbush and sage, is a pleasant feature of
alkaline valleys and plains from New Mexico and Montana
westward to Washington and California. Lewis
and Clark encountered it and set it down in their
journal, without much show of interest, as "pulpy-leaved
thorn." Douglas found it clothing "barren
grounds of the Oregon," and Frémont brought home
specimens of it from his first expedition, collected on
the upper waters of the Platte. On the strength of these
specimens Dr. Torrey dedicated the plant to Frémont
under the name *Fremontia*, as has been stated in another
chapter, but later had to withdraw this, when it transpired
that a European botanist had been ahead of him
with the name Sarcobatus, which may be freely translated
as "fleshy thorn." In contrast with the desert
sagebrush (*Artemisia tridentata*), which is an indication
of soil without alkali, this greasewood flourishes in land
containing considerable quantities of it.

Another greasewood of arid regions, but very dissimilar
to Sarcobatus, and having a more southern
range, is the famous *Larrea tridentata*, very abundant
in the Mohave and Colorado deserts of California,
eastward to Texas and southward into northern Mexico.
It is perhaps the most characteristic shrub of the arid
valleys and plains of the southwest, dotting open mesas
and the alluvial fans of cañon mouths, and filling the
air at times with a peculiar pungent aroma, which has
given rise to another common name—creosote-bush.
Mexicans call it *hediondilla*, the "little bad smeller,"
and sometimes *gobernadora*, the "governess." Why this
latter, one wonders, unless because of the plant's supposed
regulating effect on certain diseases—rheumatism
and what not—for which a decoction of the leaves and

twigs is used. The queer little sickle-shaped leaflets in
pairs are sticky with a sort of resin, which is perhaps
responsible for the antiseptic quality universally attributed by desert folk to the crushed foliage when
applied as a poultice to bruises and sores. This remedy
is especially esteemed for saddle gall; and an added
touch to the shrub's usefulness is supplied by the frequent presence of a resinous gum or lac upon the
branches, a deposit of a certain tiny scale insect.
Indians and Mexicans patiently scrape this off and
employ it as a cement for fixing arrow points, mending
broken pottery, and such matters.

According to Papago mythology, greasewood gum
played an important part in saving primal man from
obliteration. It seems that Iito, or Elder Brother, had
a premonition that the world was going to be visited
by a flood; so he made him a cask of greasewood gum
with a lid. In this quaint boat, like the Three Wise Men
of Gotham who put to sea in a bowl, this wise aboriginal
rode the flood in his boat of gum. Four times around
the world he floated, until, at last, the waters subsiding,
he landed intact in the northwest corner of Mexico,
adjoining Arizona, and there, to prove the story, the
Papagos live to this day, and told the story to Carl
Lumholtz, in whose delightful book, *New Trails in
Mexico*,[1] you will find it recorded. Often for mile upon
mile the desert traveler's way is surrounded by these
airy shrubs, well spaced one from another as though
regardful of one another's personal liberty. After
showers the bushes are soon brightly sprinkled with
solitary yellow flowers, each petal with a curious twist

[1]Carl S. Lumholtz: *New Trails in Mexico*, p. 202, Charles
Scribner's Sons, 1912.

WILD HELIO-
TROPE, or FID-
DLENECK (*Pha-
celia tanaceti-
folia*)

*Phacelia
Fremontii*

WILD BLUE LUPINE (*Lupinus affinis*)

that sets it like a miniature propeller blade, edgewise to the light. With the flowers is generally a ripening crop of the queer fuzzy white balls of seeds. This greasewood was one of the first plants to attract the notice of Frémont on his second expedition as his motley caravan passing from the Great Valley of California emerged upon the Mohave Desert. He found it "rather a graceful plant, its leaves exhaling a singular but very agreeable and refreshing odor." Succeeding explorers were not always so complimentary; Emory mentions it repeatedly with disapprobation, as so "offensive that even hungry mules will not touch it," and without value for fuel; others thought it evidence of worthless soil. This last slur upon the poor shrub has, however, been disproved, for, like the sagebrush, its presence indicates comparative freedom from alkali.

Associated with these greasewoods, and sometimes sharing in the name, are a number of gray desert shrubs properly called saltbush, from the saline flavor of the foliage. They are species of *Atriplex*, a genus of the Pigweed tribe, and distinguished usually by a peculiar white mealiness or scurfiness of the herbage, brought out very clearly by a pocket lens. The plants are exceedingly abundant on alkaline flats and mesas of the Great Basin region and the southwestern deserts, and while individually more or less homely, they often create in the mass pools of real beauty in the otherwise barren wastes that they frequent. This effect is particularly noticeable in the autumn, when the foliage and fruitful branches are painted with delicate tones of pale yellow, green and reddish brown. Especially endearing are the luscious young shoots of the stems of some species in baby pink and blue green, breathing the universal

charms of infancy. The diaries of the early exploring
expeditions in quest of a route for a transcontinental
railway make frequent mention of them under the name
of *obione*. To cattlemen, who variously call them shad-
scale, cattle-spinach, quail-brush and what not, they
are of value as forage for desert herds, and desert
Indians have to some extent utilized the seeds for
pinole, parching and grinding them for mush. The salty
young shoots of at least one species, *Atriplex lentiformis*,
the quail-bush, were boiled by the Pimas and eaten as
greens.[1]

Atriplex hymenelytra, the desert holly, has become
quite well known of recent years for its decorative
value. The silvery, prickle-edged leaves are pallid
counterparts of the true holly, and gathered in December with a sprinkling of the clustered red berries of the
desert mistletoe, which grows in parasitic "witch-
brooms" on mesquite and a few other shrubs, they make
you a unique Christmas wreath indeed. The desert holly
is native to washes and gravelly hillsides of the Mohave
and Colorado deserts eastward to Utah and Arizona,
and was first described from specimens collected by
Arthur Schott of the Mexican Boundary Survey, whose
name is linked with a number of desert plants. Apropos
of the ornamental worth of these desert Atriplexes,
I find it interesting to learn that two species—*A. canescens*, shad-scale, and *A. confertifolia*, sheep-fat—have
been cultivated for years at the Royal Botanic Gardens
at Kew, where they are objects of curiosity to British
eyes because of their whitish foliage, all the whiter, I
fancy, in contrast with the surrounding green of that
moist land.

[1]Standley: *Trees and Shrubs of Mexico*, p. 252.

Of yet another greasewood—one that is exceedingly abundant throughout cismontane California—something has been said in a previous chapter, Adenostoma of the rose family.

CHAPTER XXXI

*Of Some Desert Notables and Oddities Not Already
Mentioned.*

Spring comes early to the Colorado Desert of California, and shortly after New Year one may expect to find on warm mesas and hill slopes the first fiery blossoms tipping the spiny, wand-like stems of the Ocotillo, *Fouquieria splendens.* Nothing delights my erudite neighbor, the Professor, more than to be asked by some newcomer to the desert how this queer word ocotillo came to be, for he believes he knows. "Don't pronounce it as though it rhymed with pillow," he will say oracularly, "but *ocotee-yo.* The word is a Spanish graft on an Aztec root, for the plant is native not only to our southwest but also far down in Old Mexico. In the ancient speech of the Montezumas certain species of pines native to Mexico were called *ocotl.* The Aztecs would split this wood, which is very resinous, into splints; then setting fire to one end they had a torch that served to light them about—a practice that still prevails to some extent among the poorer classes in parts of Mexico, who meantime have softened the original name of the tree to *ocote.* Now it was found that the wood of the shrub Fouquieria, especially the bark, is similarly resinous and gummy, and burns readily like *ocote,* with a pleasant fragrance. So it, too, was collected, cut into lengths of a foot or so, and when dried made a good

292

Toyon (*Photinia arbutifolia*)

Tree Mallow (*Lavatera assurgentiflora*)

SAGEBRUSH (*Artemisia tridentata*) in the Sierra Madre, California

substitute for the *ocote* splints. Naturally enough, it has acquired the *ocote's* name with the diminutive *illo* affixed, that is, *ocotillo,* which merely means 'little *ocote'* or 'little pine.'"

The Ocotillo is useful in other ways, too. A very general purpose to which the strong stems are put is the making of fences, and the walls of Indian huts. The stems are cut into suitable lengths and set side by side, with one end thrust deep into the earth. If an irrigation ditch happens to be near, many will take root, leaf out and flourish like Joseph's staff. Whether from some such association, imperfectly remembered, or from the fact that walking sticks are often made of the hard, heavy wood, the name Jacob's staff is sometimes given to the plant; as also is coach-whip, evident enough from the whip-like shoots. Still another is candle-wood, obviously from the use of the dried stems as lights. Yet another use seems to have been a monopoly of the Coahuilla Indians. These aborigines, to quote Barrows, whose treatise on the ethno-botany of that people is a classic, used to eat the sugary flowers, as well as to make a sweet beverage by soaking them in water.[1] The spines of the plant have a special interest—they are the foot-stalks of the stem's first leaves. These leaves soon drop, leaving the foot-stalks naked which, under the harsh conditions of their environment, harden into thorns. Later a new crop of neat little leaves is born, which nestle in rosettes in the elbows of the stem and thorns, disappearing in droughty weather, and being re-born after showers. Naturally, the Ocotillo is generally

[1] David Prescott Barrows: *The Ethno-Botany of the Coahuilla Indians of Southern California,* University of Chicago Press, 1900.

leafless, as droughtiness is the normal state of its desert home.

Mexico is the mother of Fouquieria, the home of the seven known species, only one of which, our Ocotillo, extends beyond the Mexican borders. The discovery of this species is credited to Dr. A. Wislizenius, a celebrated botanist, who made a trip in 1848 from Missouri to northern Mexico by way of Santa Fe. In traversing the terrible desert of southern New Mexico known as *La Jornada del Muerto* (the Journey of the Dead) he found a curious, puzzling plant, all spines and stems, many from the same root. Later on, south of the Rio Grande, flowering stems were encountered, enabling the identity of the plant to be determined—a new member of the genus Fouquieria, of which Humboldt long before had discovered two species in Mexico, and given it a name in honor of a French professor of medicine at Paris, Dr. Pierre Ed. Fouquier.

Leaves in desert plant society are by no means *de rigueur*. While some plants are quite conventional in that regard, and enfoliage themselves completely, others, like the Ocotillo, are scantily—even intermittently—clothed; and others, again, will have nothing to do with leaves, and appear, openly and unashamed, naked to the world. A plant of the latter sort, the Spaniards, with their remarkable genius for apropos descriptive terms, have been known to call *palo de Adán*, that is, such as Adam was before he became self-conscious. Of the latter class are the various species of Ephedra, humble relative of the pine and fir. In the speech of the people they are variously known as joint-fir, desert tea, Mexican tea, squaw tea, teamster's tea, *cañatilla*, *tepopote*, *popotillo* and what not.

Naturally such a string of vernacular names betokens a popular interest in the plant, surprising on first acquaintance, for Ephedra is a homely subject, poor in esthetic appeal, and quite unlike any other North American plant. One description fits fairly well all of the four species found on the California desert, the specific differences being slight to the layman's eye— erect shrubs composed of a mass of slender green pointed stems with branches clustered at the stem joints, like witches' brooms, and never a leaf. As for flowers, desert folk, whose idea of a flower is something showy in red or yellow, will tell you there are none, and as a matter of fact they are scarcely noticeable, an insignificant matter of naked stamens and pistils of brief duration.

Stem and branches are another story. In them the interest centers, and it is purely economic. Somehow, at some time, Indians and Mexicans—for the plant is abundant in northern Mexico—learned that a tonic tea could be brewed of them, of service in sundry miseries of the flesh. In the years when our West was being conquered, desert tea sprang into special favor on the frontier as a remedy for the so-called "French disease," that shameful by-product of the white man's intrusion into primitive cultures the world over. From this fact one species abundant in the southwestern deserts was called botanically *Ephedra antisyphilitica*. The astringency in all our species imparts a certain tang to the tea that makes it a pleasant beverage to robust palates, and it is much consumed by cowboys and desert dwellers in general. Only the other day I read of a convention of ladies gathered in some desert town, where the refreshment served was squaw tea.

The stems may be used either green or dried, and are immersed in boiling water for such number of minutes as may be needful to bring out the flavor in desired strength.

There is a suspicion that our knowledge of Ephedra's peculiar qualities may be due to Mexican contact with the Chinese before our southwest became ours; for it is a matter of record that Chinese doctors have employed an Asiatic species of Ephedra in their practice for more than forty centuries. They call it *ma-huang*, and prescribe it for colds, fever, headaches and skin eruptions caused by poisons in the blood.[1] Within the last few years, our own medical men have become interested in it, and a drug known as ephedrine is to be had of pharmacists. The first California species, which occurs sparingly on both the Mohave and Colorado deserts, but frequently east of the Colorado River as far as Texas, was *Ephedra trifurca*, collected by Lieutenant Emory in the autumn of 1846 in southern New Mexico.

Abundant on sandy desert mesas, as well as on dry plains and in washes of coastal California, is the wild rhubarb or pie-plant—*Rumex hymenosepalus*,[2] which attracts notice early in the year by its great rosy panicles of clustered seed vessels, simulating bloom. The ruddy leaf stalks are acid, tender and juicy, and make an excellent substitute for garden rhubarb, to which this plant is close akin. Wild rhubarb pie is one of the choicest delicacies the desert housewife can offer, and

[1]Groff and Clark: *The Botany of Ephedra*. University of California Press, Berkeley, 1928.

[2]*Hymen*, a membrane, *sepalus*, a sepal, from the membranous inner divisions of the flower's calyx, which cling to the seeds, and give to the flower panicle its showy color.

it will deceive an epicure. And this is not all. The tuberous roots, clustered like a dahlia's, have their secret,
too. Crushed, they yield a permanent dye, formerly
employed by Navajo blanket weavers to stain wool
yellow. Moreover, these roots are rich in tannin, and an
even more important use of them by the Mexican
population, who call the plant *cañaigre*, or *cañágria*,
was in tanning hides. Their efficiency in this respect
attracted the acquisitive Gringo, and attempts were
made to cultivate cañaigre in southern California some
years ago on a commercial scale. It was found, however,
that the plant did not respond cheerfully to domestic
life, and irrigation reduced the tannin content, so the
rainbow faded before the pot of gold was found. Spanish
Californian children peeled the juicy stems and ate them
with relish, as they did cacomites, the Brodiaea's bulbs.

A member of the same family with wild rhubarb—the
Buckwheat tribe—is the remarkable desert trumpet,
Eriogonum inflatum, discovered by Frémont in 1844
during his passage of the Mohave Desert, its leafless
stems providing an occasional meager snack to the
expedition's half-starved live stock. It is a plant of an
inconstant habit, varying from six inches in height to
three feet, with a curious bulging leafless stem, which
at the summit branches and forks and forks again into a
diffuse lacy crown, spraying out in the spring into tiny
yellow flowers. It then presents the appearance of a fairy
tree, with a trunk full to bursting. Nevertheless, it does
not burst, but, the seed once set, dies most convention-
ally in bed, that is, where rooted, its lively green paling
to an ivory white. The outer twiggage, however, with its
burden of seeds, is blown hither and yon about the
desert. Months later one finds the pallid dropsical stem

standing dismantled and wonders of what it can be the ghost. Dr. Coville, who collected the species on the mountains bordering Death Valley in the course of his famous expedition there in 1890–1891, states that these dead inflated stalks, bleached yellowish white, gave rise to the popular name "cigarette-plant"—a name, by the way, I recently heard for it on the Colorado Desert.

Eriogonum inflatum is a common plant on all our deserts, and the late Mr. S. B. Parish once informed me that he found people gathering it while the inflated stem, which is somewhat acid, was still young and tender, to be eaten green like a pickle; so "pickles" they called the plant. The genus Eriogonum is characteristically western, one of the many that give the charm of novelty to the plant lover's first visit to the Pacific slope. About a hundred species and varieties are indigenous to California, denizens mostly of deserts, dry valleys and arid mesas and mountains. One species particularly abundant throughout southern California, and northward along the desert slopes of the mountains into Nevada, is the well known wild buckwheat, or flat-top *Eriogonum fasciculatum.* Bees value it highly, and the honey produced from it ranks with the very finest, being one of the main dependencies of the honey makers during the dry mid-year, when other flowers are scarce. The tiny flowers of the Eriogonums, clustered in heads or umbels, attain in many species to ornamental value through sheer force of numbers. Usually white or pink, they are occasionally yellow. Of the last color is *E. umbellatum,* the sulphur-flower, a charming creation, with several long stalks and clover-like heads of clear yellow blossoms. Its habitat extends from the

Pacific Coast Ranges eastward to the Rocky Mountains. From the latter region specimens were early
carried to the Atlantic coast and thence to England,
introduced there as long ago as 1811, where it is regarded
as a choice subject for rock gardens.

On the arid mountain slopes of eastern San Diego
County overlooking the desert are the immemorial
mescal pits of the Diegueño Indians. Even yet the
region is visited every March by old Indians, remnants
of their tribe, to camp out and cut and bake mescal, to
sing the old songs and dance the old dances under the
stars and tell again the tales of the ancients. Mescal
(the form in which the Aztec word *mexcalli* has reached
California) is the general name for various species of
Agave, of which three or four are native to the California deserts. *Agave deserti* and its similar associated
species *consociata* resemble small editions of the familiar
century plant, or maguey, of Mexico, notorious mother
of pulque and the fiery tequila. The plants are gregarious
and grow in large circular assemblages.

Of the California species the Indians made a notable
food, and the manner of preparing it was this: For
many years, a dozen or so, the mescal is merely a rosette
of stiff, spiny leaves set close to the ground and as
unemotional as a cactus. Then one spring, the universal
impulse to produce seed and multiply in the earth
greatly thrills even this stolid plant. In the heart of it
appears a stout bud like a Brobdingnagian asparagus
sprout, which, after attaining the height of six inches or
so, is ripe for having its head snipped off. A shallow pit
is dug in the gravelly ground, lined with stones, and
heated by a bonfire of wood selected with care to avoid
any bitter sort. A number of mescal butts are then

smothered in the hot ashes, covered with earth, and the whole allowed to steam for a day and a night. On opening the pit on the morrow the mescal is trimmed of its charred exterior, and, behold, a brown juicy mass, sweet as molasses and very nutritious for men and women of sound livers. Indians, who as a race are sweet-toothed, were—and are—extravagantly fond of it, and after a feast on the spot would pack up the remainder and carry it home to their rancherías for consumption later. Unmolested flower stalks grow to a height of eight, ten or twelve feet, or even more, with blobs of pale yellow bloom on short branches at the top. This, too, was meat to the Indians, at least the Coahuillas of the San Jacinto region, who, according to Dr. Barrows, boiled and ate the flowers. The mescal leaves are rich in fiber, which the old-time Indians would thresh out and make into ropes, bowstrings, sandals and such matters.

Lieutenant Emory's party encountered miles of mescal—Centennial plant, they called it—as they approached the California Cordillera from the desert. The needle-pointed leaves were a sore trial to his ragged, more or less bare-legged troopers, who, however, got some solace from the plants, according to the official report, by cutting them and using the "body of them" as food—an eloquent commentary on the state of the expedition's larder at the time.

Another of Emory's collections was a plant that quickly attracts everyone's attention, and was named by Dr. Asa Gray *Encelia farinosa*. The pioneer Coulter had got it a decade before, but no one had given it a name. It is a low, dome-shaped bush, with whitish stems and silvery-gray foliage—a plant noticeable for its very whiteness at whatever time of year, but in late winter

A desert wild garden, slope of Santa Rosa Mountains, California. The plants at extreme left are *Incienso*; Biznaga (Barrel Cactus) center, Ocotillo to right of it; Mescal in middle foreground and extreme right: all plants of economic worth.

and spring, all glorious with a crown of golden bloom, like small sunflowers, lifted well above the foliage on slender stalks. After the ripening of the flowers these stalks dry into pallidness, too. The bush occurs on the deserts from Death Valley southward in increasing abundance on both sides of the Colorado River and of the Gulf of California. Dr. Hornaday, in a trip a quarter century ago through southwestern Arizona and adjacent Mexico, of which he told the story in a delightful book, *Camp Fires on Desert and Lava*, fell in love with this beautiful thing, and finding it in need of a good English name, christened it white brittlebush, from the dry, brittle flower stalks, a handful of which he could snap as easily as so many clay pipe stems.

Long before that, however, it had received various names in Mexico—as *palo blanco* (white stick), *hierba ceniza* (the herb of ashes), *hierba del vaso*, and *incienso*. The last two vernacularisms need a special explanation. A close inspection of this bush reveals small exudations of a yellow resinous gum from the stems and trunk. These may often be gathered in considerable quantity from the ground beneath the shrub, in the form of globules or nuggets, and if a match be touched to them they will burn freely, giving off a pungent fragrance. The late T. S. Brandegee, who botanized extensively in Lower California a generation or two ago, found this gum being collected and burned as incense in the churches, for which reason the plant was called *incienso*. From this same gum-bearing habit *hierba del vaso* derives, and the explorer Carl Lumholtz, in *New Trails in Mexico*, tells why. It seems that Mexicans with a pain in the left side warm the gum and smear it on the body below the ribs (they call that part of the human frame

vaso) to relieve the distress, and consider it more efficacious than any porous plaster. Lumholtz also saw
Papago children using it as chewing gum and their elders
making a varnish of it. Add to these uses the obvious
one of making firewood of its resinous branches, and you
will realize that the bush is of real importance in the
arid regions it inhabits. And then, the beauty of it!

Once in a while on a desert ramble you may find your
ankles held tight by a pair of queer, curving black claws
in the form of a pair of tongs, joined at the base to a seed
vessel of some sort. This is the dry fruit of the Martynia,
the so-called devil's claw, occurring in two or three
species from southern California, eastward to Texas and
Mexico. They are a weedy, clammy sort of herb with
rather large, baggy flowers, yellowish or purplish,
blooming in the summer, followed in autumn by the
curious pods, their slender beaks well on to a foot long
and curved upward. When dry this beak splits into a
pair of elastic hooked horns—the curves facing each
other—the tongs that caught your legs so securely just
now. Mexicans, finding their horses' legs similarly
clasped, and their sheep's woolly coats worse tangled by
the spiny affairs, call the pods in their exasperation
espuela del diablo, devil's spur. In placider moments the
resemblance to a bull's head with long diverging horns
has inspired the milder figure *torito*, little bull.

Martynia in California is indigenous only on the
Colorado Desert in the species *Martynia altheaefolia*—
that is althea-leaved. Lower California has it much more
abundantly, and it was there, on the shores of Magdalena Bay, that it was first discovered nearly a century
ago by the botanist Hinds of H. M. S. *Sulphur*, which
touched there in the autumn of 1839 on an exploring

expedition. The Pima and Papago Indians of southern Arizona use the outer fiber of the Martynia horns for weaving the black designs of their famous baskets. By the way, do not think unkindly of the poor plant as you untangle its horns from your legs. The Lord arranged it so, in order that its seeds should be spread abroad and other places than the place of its birth should know it too.

And speaking of such entangling alliances, a word may be said about Mentzelia, a large genus of western American herbaceous plants, often with shining white stems, of which our Pacific coast has a dozen different species, denizens of gravelly washes, arid hillsides and the deserts. Several bear fine showy flowers, one or two of which have found a permanent place in gardens both in this country and abroad. The rather brittle leaves are more or less covered with short barbed hairs, which hook themselves tenaciously to the clothing of passers-by, dragging the leaves with them until one's legs are plastered with them. Spanish-speaking people, with dry humor, call them *buena mujer*, that is good woman, because they stick to a man with constancy. A beautiful species found almost throughout California and parts of Oregon in dry, rocky stream beds is *Mentzelia laevicaulis*, the smooth-stemmed, with magnificent creamy yellow flowers four or five inches across. The five slender-pointed petals, full spread at evening's approach around a central mass of bristling stamens, suggest a great star and have earned for the plant the common name, blazing star. It was a discovery of Douglas's on the upper Columbia, and it is one of the species sometimes found in gardens.

Another blazing star more often seen in cultivation

is *Mentzelia Lindleyi*, the flowers not quite so large, but of a rich golden color with a vermilion heart. It also was discovered by Douglas, who found it somewhere in central California, where it still occurs within a limited area, opening in full sunshine. Douglas's seeds were liberally distributed, and before long the gardens of Britain, even to the Scotch Highlands, blazed with the handsome flower. It is still cultivated abroad as well as in the United States.

The distinguished English botanist John Lindley named the plant *Bartonia aurea*, a name that preserves the memory of Dr. Benjamin Smith Barton of the University of Pennsylvania, one of the earliest writers on American botany. Later study by Torrey and Gray convinced these botanists that it was improperly classed as a Bartonia, and placing it in the genus Mentzelia they at the same time, by way of polite recognition, added Lindley's name for specific distinction.

CHAPTER XXXII

A Handful of California Weeds; of Anís Hinojo,
Our Lady's Thistle, Filaree and Puncture Weed;
and Some Other Hoboes of the Plant World.

Hoeing in my garden one day I suddenly became conscious of a faint fragrance suggestive of ripe apples. I discovered that it was given off by some small weeds that my hoe was scraping up.

"Now here," thought I, "is a very Christian among weeds, returning the soft answer of a sweet perfume to my death strokes—doing good with its last breath to my despiteful usage."

They were low-growing plants with finely cut leaves and greenish-yellow flower heads, egg-shaped and without evident petals; and in fact just such homely weeds, except for that saving grace of fragrance, as anyone would naturally want to get rid of. I remembered seeing them growing in great numbers in city parkings and along roadsides in the country, but now that pleasant perfume, noticed for the first time, interested me in them.

I took a specimen into my library, where in a botanical manual I worked out its name. It proved to be the fragrant Matricaria, a close relative of that herb out of which our grandmothers made the camomile tea supposed to be good for us when our stomachs were out of sorts, and has quite a little history.

Lewis and Clark met it on the banks of the Kooskooskie in Idaho, and Pursh gave it a name, based on their specimens. "A small plant with an agreeable smell," he remarks in his *Flora*. The land of its origin has proved to be almost as much of a puzzle as that of the American Indian. The weight of authority, I believe, leans to its being a native of the Pacific Northwest, with a good second supporting northern Asia as its cradle. From one or the other center—or possibly from both— the courageous little plant has traveled east and west, now and then settling by the way, prospering and then starting out again, its seeds given rides by birds and animals and railway trains, until at last it has completely circled the globe, and is even quite at home in such out-of-the-way lands as Chile and New Zealand.

Rather a noteworthy achievement when you come to think of it—is it not?—for an unrecommended plantlet with never a human hand voluntarily held out to help, solely achieving through its own pluck and unobtrusive perseverance. In a botanic way it has realized the beatitude of the meek and has inherited the earth.

In California Matricaria loves the neighborhood of old cattle corrals and barns, and for a few weeks each spring clothes waste places about towns with a cheerful verdure. The pleasant fragrance given off by the bruised herbage has gained for it the common name pineapple-weed. The Spanish-speaking population call it *manzanilla*, little apple, and have long included it in their domestic pharmacopœia. In old times, when the herb was fully mature, that is, in April or May, it would be gathered, dried in the sun, and crushed to a powder. This would be put in a jar and set away, until some luckless youngster (or oldster, for that matter) would be taken with a stomach-ache, when a pinch of *manza-nilla* would be made into a tea and administered. "An *ex*-cellent, *ex*-cellent thing," my friend Doña Matilde Carteri tells me, "*cosa excelentísima!*"

Indeed, many a weed that we ruthlessly destroy has an interesting history. For instance, there is fennel, *Foeniculum vulgare*, found in waste places on both the Pacific and Atlantic seaboards. In summer, a time of year when most wild flowers in the California valleys and lowlands are taking their annual rest, the fennel's flat umbels of mustard-yellow bloom make a lovely show along the roadside and country lanes. It is a tall herb with bluish-green stems, often the height of a man, and thread-like leaves, which when crushed give off the fragrance of licorice. You probably know it by its common misnomer in California, sweet anise, or by the children's name, lady's chewing tobacco. Its original home was in Europe, and its introduction into America was due, they say, to the esteem in which the seeds were held as a household remedy for digestive troubles. On the Pacific coast its occurrence may very reasonably be attributed to the Franciscan missionaries to whom we are indebted for so many Old World plants. It is certain that the leaves crushed in water were used to sprinkle the floors of the mission church at San Juan Capistrano to make them smell sweet. The Spanish Californians, who call the plant *anís hinojo*, or simply *hinojo*, would formerly mingle the feathery foliage with their bouquets, as we use smilax or *asparagus plumosus;* and the juicy stems they would munch as people in the tropics chew sugar-cane. So Doña Matilde tells me. "But now," she adds, "it is not so. My daughters won't eat *hinojo* stems. And do you know why? It's because they have so much fruit to eat nowadays; but that is better. We Spanish in old times had little fruit, and so we ate *hinojo*." Nevertheless, Fennel is not neglected, in southern California, at least. The other day an Armenian told me that the tender young shoots are gathered by his people, who cook them like spinach and serve with egg—a practice imported from their Old World home. My neighbor, the Professor, adds to this that in Sicily the donkeys rejoice in the sweet juicy stems, so that the peasantry of that country call the plant donkey hay.

Among the thistles, always most execrated of weeds, several have a place in the interest of the lover of old tales. One of these, an immigrant from the Mediterranean region, is the purple-flowered milk thistle, or our lady's thistle, *Silybum marianum*, distinguished by remarkable white blotchings along the leaf veins, which popular tradition in Europe explains as the persistent stains from droppings of milk from Mary's breast as she nursed the infant Christ. This thistle has become a dreaded nuisance to agriculturists on our Pacific coast, more particularly in central California, where it appeared as early as 1853.

In much the same class is the star thistle, *Centaurea solstitialis*, also a European immigrant. Its tiny yellow blossoms are like the tip of a brush protruding from a globular base set with bristling spines sometimes an inch long. You will see it on vacant lots, by neglected roadsides, and in cultivated lands, particularly in the Sacramento Valley, where it is a serious pest. The title of "thistle" is readily conceded to so prickly a plant, but you may wonder where the "star" comes in. In the Middle Ages, it seems, there was in use a military weapon consisting of a metal ball armed all about with sharp spikes and fastened frequently upon the end of a staff. It was called with grim humor morning star. The resemblance of our weed-flower, with its rotund, spiny involucre, to this weapon is striking enough to have suggested the name to some ancient herbalist, and it has stuck in the popular speech of two worlds.[1] It also goes by the name of Barnaby's thistle, from its flowering about the time of St. Barnabas Day, June 11th. This in the Old Style calendar is equivalent to the modern June 22d, the time of the summer solstice, and so we have the explanation of that specific name *solstitialis*. Similar in appearance, but with smaller flowers and shorter spines, is the still commoner Napa thistle, first introduced at Napa, California, according to Jepson, and diffused over the state in seed grain. It too is from Europe—*Centaurea melitensis*, that is, of Melita, the modern Malta, where among other places the plant grew from of old. It would not have been strange if St. Paul, shipwrecked on Melita, had picked it up along with the viper in that bundle of sticks with which he mended the fire that had been kindled to warm the shivering company.

Another of our troublesome weeds whose name has a military flavor is the ground caltrop from Europe. It is a small, yellow-flowered, creeping plant of sandy waste places, and bears a bur-like seed vessel of a vicious sort with four prominent spines. The resemblance of the pod is quite marked to the caltrop of ancient warfare, an iron ball with four protruding spikes, which was thrown in numbers on the ground to impede the advance of cavalry—a sort of forerunner of the modern barbed-wire

[1]Prior: *Popular Names of British Plants.*

entanglement. The Romans called the thing *tribulus*, a name which modern botanists have adopted for the plant, specifically *Tribulus terrestris*. It began to be noticed in California about the year 1900 along railway tracks and about freight yards. The long, trailing stems have a propensity to creep out upon the roadway, where the wheels of bicycles and automobiles pick up the spiny burs, thus not only spreading the weed, but incidentally often puncturing the tires that carry them —a vicious, ungrateful weed, indeed. On this account the old name, ground caltrop, has been superseded by the more obvious puncture-weed. With the growing vogue of air travel the spread of the pest is still further increased by airplanes, which carry it on their wheels.

A weed in which good and bad are mixed is the wild oat, *Avena fatua*. This is abundant in fields and waste places from parts of the middle west to the Pacific coast. Its seed differs from the cultivated grain in being armed with brown bristles which stick in the throat of animals and bring distress to the eater, very much as the course of youthful folly in humanity called "sowing one's wild oats" is followed by a painful harvest of trouble in later years. Nevertheless, it is believed from this vexatious weed there has been developed the smooth-hulled oat-grain that is a staple food of man and beast. How the wild oat ever reached California is not certainly known, but it is pretty definitely established that the southern end of the state knew it first. Doubtless the original grain arrived by way of Mexico tangled in the wool of Spanish sheep. Once started it spread rapidly over the great valleys and open hillsides, till now it clothes half of California with its verdure in the spring. Old-time travelers spoke of a growth so lush sometimes that a man on horseback would be hidden in it. Dr. J. S. Newberry, botanist of a Pacific Railroad survey in 1855, stated that throughout central and southern California at that time, wherever the ground was not in forest, wild oats covered hundreds of miles as completely as grasses covered the prairies of Illinois.

A widely distributed plant in California that is considered a weed in certain places and esteemed for its forage value in others is the so-called filaree, or Erodium. Every California child knows its pretty rosettes of fern-like leaves that hug the winter earth of old lawns and dooryards, bare valley lands, mesas and open hillsides, even on the deserts and far away eastward. Under the stimulation of the rains, they develop pretty clusters of starry flowers, small and rosy-lilac, and these are followed by seed vessels with an inch-long slender beak resembling a pin, on which account the Spanish people called the plant *alfilerillo* (pronounced *alfileree-yo*), which the usual American fashion of short-cutting has reduced to filaree, gringo-ized into pin clover. On ripening, the seed vessel splits and shoots out the seeds—each with a tiny hook in its nose and a tail with successive tight coils like a corkscrew, ending in a sickle-like flourish. Children long ago discovered that if they placed a seed on a damp cloth or a wet penny, or even on the palm of a moist hand, the corkscrew tail would begin to untwist and the sickle end would slowly turn round like the hands of a clock. So "clocks" came to be the children's name for filaree seeds. Falling to the ground, the seeds similarly deport themselves and screw their way gradually into the earth, the process being

promoted by the alternating dryness of day and the
moisture of night, the latter straightening out the tail,
the former curling it up again.⌋

There are two species of filaree, the red-stemmed
Erodium cicutarium—that is, the hemlock-leaved—and
E. moschatum, with lusher, somewhat musky-scented
foliage.⌊Both species are natives of the Mediterranean
region, and may have been brought to California by
the Franciscan missionaries on account of their value
as forage plants. At any rate, they must have arrived
here well on to a century ago, and, once here, the
character of the seeds admirably adapted them to
lodgment on the backs of Spanish sheep and cattle,
which spread them from San Diego northward. Frémont, arriving in the Sacramento Valley in the spring
of 1844, found the ground covered with *Erodium cicutarium*, "like a sward of grass," and Indian women
gathered it into large conical baskets for food.⌋

⌈In the southern end of the San Joaquin Valley, its
advance was also noteworthy. "Instead of grass," the
journal records, "the whole face of the country is closely
covered with *Erodium cicutarium*, here only two or three
inches high. Its height and beauty varied in a remarkable manner with the locality, being, in many places
. . . around streams and springs, two and three feet
high." Evidently both species were found, and both
have played an important part in feeding the cattle of
Spanish Californians and Americans, being relished by
stock both when green and withered on the ground.

In spite of all the harsh things that may be said of
weeds, I find it interesting to know, as the late S. B.
Parish pointed out in one of his papers,[1] that it is to

[1] *Zoe*, 1:9.

the plant-eradicating sheep—John Muir's "hoofed locusts"—which have destroyed so much of our native
flora, that California, in all likelihood, owes the introduction of her three most abundant and valuable forage
plants—the filaree, the bur-clover and the wild oat; for
the last, in spite of the vices of its maturity, affords,
when young, a good pasturage, and in the early days
was extensively harvested for hay. As for bur-clover
(*Medicago hispida*), this is a lowly little member of the
Pea family, which flashes its small bright yellow blossom, like glints of gold, amid the first green carpeting
of spring throughout California. It, too, is a native of
the Mediterranean region, and probably came in with
the Spanish missionaries, for travelers in the early
American period of the state found it abundant everywhere. Its value as forage is greatest when naturally
cured on the ground, at which time its stems are clothed
with the curious prickly burs or seed vessels, to which,
with the clover-like foliage, the plant owes its common
name. These burs, in spite of the prickles, are consumed
by stock with obvious relish, even licked up from the
bare ground—an amazing sight to the tenderfoot, who
sees the earth but not the burs.

The coming of these immigrant weeds, together with
others as aggressive, notably the Brome-grasses, marks
a new era in the history of our native wild flowers,
comparable in a way to the case of aboriginal man when
his immemorial home was broken into by the invading
whites. Wherever the latter's agricultural and industrial
operations have taken place, the foreign weed flora has
sprung up, become naturalized and increasingly crowded
out the more delicate indigenes. For these, now, we must
seek ever farther and farther afield—in the hills, the

arroyo washes, the deserts and those blessed sanctuaries the national forests. But while even among the flowers the old order passes, beauty does not; though man has invented the word weed, Nature has fashioned the plant, and she does all things well.

INDEX